97386

QA
75
.M78

Mullish, Henry

How to use a
pocket calculator

How to Use  a Pocket  Calculator

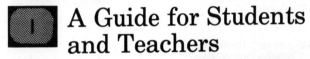

A Guide for Students and Teachers

By
Henry Mullish

Arco Publishing Company, Inc.
New York

Published by Arco Publishing Company, Inc.
219 Park Avenue South, New York, N.Y. 10003

Library of Congress Cataloging in Publication Data

Mullish, Henry.
  How to use a pocket calculator—A guide for the modern student.

  1. Calculating-machines—Problems, exercises, etc.
I. Title.

QA75.M78   510'.28   76-28333
ISBN 0-668-04081-5 (Library Edition)
ISBN 0-668-04072-6 (Paper Edition)

Printed in the United States of America

This book is dedicated to my nephew

Adrian

Acknowledgments

It is with great pleasure and gratitude that I recognize the important contribution made by Steve Kochan of the State University of New York at Buffalo, who collaborated wholeheartedly in the preparation of this book. This is not the first time that he has cooperated in this fashion in the writing of a book, and it is my firm belief that neither is it the last.

I would also like to express my deep appreciation to David Blaustein of New York University, who helped in the formulation of the sections on chemistry and physics and in the preparation of the answers for these sections.

Contents

1

Introduction

A revolution is taking place across the United States and indeed throughout the world. In this revolution nobody is getting killed and no government is being overthrown. It is a silent revolution, one whose only sound is the clicking of the keys of electronic pocket calculators, those magnificent, pocket-sized tools that calculate with unbelievable accuracy at phenomenal speed and at modest expense.

These calculators are a direct result of the space age. The new technology which makes them possible—called *large-scale integrated (LSI) circuitry*—was first developed as part of the effort to put a man on the moon. LSI circuitry makes it possible to crowd up to 10,000 microscopic transistors onto a piece of silicon less than $\frac{1}{16}$-inch square, thus greatly reducing the size and weight of complex electronic machinery. One of these tiny, complex networks is called a *chip*.

The first calculators utilizing chips came on the scene in 1971 and sold for about $400. Since then, there have been many improvements and prices have plummeted. Different models have multiplied so rapidly that today there are about five hundred available—and each one can be carried in a shirt pocket.

During the brief time that the pocket calculator has been available, many uses have been found for it, both on the job and in everyday life. This book is concerned with the possibilities that the calculator has for high school and college students. It describes the different features that calculators may have and shows how these features can best be utilized in doing the calculations required in mathematics and science courses.

Since there are so many different models manufactured, each with its own particular set of features, in this book we shall describe the functions and operations of three basic models which are widely used and easily obtainable. These models have been carefully selected to illustrate the various levels of complexity which modern pocket calculators possess. They represent calculators ranging in price from under \$20 up to about \$100. This range encompasses both the ordinary "four-function" calculator and the sophisticated "super-scientific" calculator, which is of such immense value to the mathematician, the scientist, and the research worker. We shall discuss in detail the difference between algebraic logic and so-called reverse Polish notation (RPN), which is used not only by some of the more sophisticated calculators but also by a popular line selling for well under \$50.

Since the three basic types we shall concentrate upon represent the broad range of available models, no matter what calculator you have—or borrow, or buy—you will be able to relate the information in this book to it and thereby increase both your range of applications and your expertise with the calculator. The techniques you learn will reinforce many of the concepts you will be studying at one stage or another, and thus the calculator will become a learning aid of immeasurable value.

The calculator can also be an experimental tool, one that enables you to derive considerable insight into the field of mathematics. Did it ever occur to you that the reciprocal of the reciprocal of a number is that original number itself? Or that 2.56% of 27.89 is equivalent to 27.89% of 2.56? (Yes, percentages are also—as mathematicians say—*commutative*. That is to say, $A\%$ of B is equal to $B\%$ of A.)

But don't think that there is general agreement that calculators are a good thing. Opinion is sharply divided on this question. There are those who believe that students should be forced to calculate everything, either in their heads, with pencil and paper, or with tables. Otherwise, they fear, the brain will atrophy. Such people seem to worry about a time in the distant future when a group of scientists will gather around the remains of a twentieth-century man and wonder what possible function the brain must have served in the past, as if it had turned into some kind of cranial appendix!

There is no question that excessive reliance on the calculator for minor calculations could be detrimental to mental efficiency, but sensible people act with restraint, with reason, and with common sense. They will use the calculator only when there is a real need for it and thereby gain maximum advantage from it.

With the aid of a pocket calculator lengthy calculations which might otherwise be quite tedious and burdensome can be dealt with quickly and precisely. In many cases the chore may even be converted into fun. This is particularly true for students to whom numbers in any shape or form are intimidating.

It is in the elementary school that the foundations of mathematics are laid and that manual calculation is taught and drilled. It is important for students to master these techniques so that, in a pinch, they can solve ordinary problems with pencil and paper, or even in their heads. Beyond elementary school, however, where increasingly difficult concepts are taught, the calculator can be used to free students from the burden of calculation and permit them to concentrate on the concepts and principles that they must thoroughly understand in order to do superior work.

2
The Basic Calculator

By far the most common of all pocket calculators is the four-function calculator, which has keys that permit the user to add, subtract, multiply, and divide instantaneously. Sometimes there is an additional function, such as a percentage key, a square root key, or a reciprocal key. All of these keys are always plainly visible on the keyboard. Another feature which such a calculator might possess, but which is *not* visible on the keyboard, is an automatic constant. This useful feature will be explained in section 2.2.

We have selected as our basic calculator model one which has the standard eight-digit display, a floating decimal point (meaning that the calculator places the decimal point in its correct position automatically), is battery operated (it is powered by two standard AA disposable batteries), operates with algebraic logic (2 plus 3 is keyed in as 2 + 3 =), has separate keys marked ⊞ , ⊟ , ⊠ , ⊡ , and ⊟ , has a percentage key marked ⍰ , and, most importantly, is available across the nation for well under $20. Such a calculator is the Casio Pocket-Mini (model number CP-801C), which is popular, widely advertised, and representative of dozens of commonly used calculators. The Pocket-Mini has an automatic constant. However, whether or not your calculator has a percentage key or an automatic constant, the information to be found in this book will prove to be both interesting and useful.

A picture of our basic calculator appears on page 16.

Once the machine is switched on, the number 0. enters the display panel, which is sometimes referred to as the "X-register." To add 2 + 3, we first key in 2, which replaces 0 in the display. Next, we hit the $\boxed{+}$ key; 2 remains in the display (the X-register), but it is also transmitted to an inner register called the "Y-register," where it is "stored." We then key in 3, the number to be added to 2, and it replaces 2 in the display. Finally, hitting the $\boxed{=}$ key causes the contents of the X- and Y-registers to be added (2 + 3), and the result (5.) is displayed in the X-register.

Once you have mastered addition, the other three operations become just as easy. The $\boxed{-}$ key is used for subtraction, the $\boxed{\times}$ key for multiplication, and the $\boxed{\div}$ key for division.

Just for practice, calculate the following expressions and compare your answers with those at the bottom of the page. (Incidentally, when going from one calculation to the next, it is not necessary to clear the machine, although it's certainly not wrong to do so.)

1. 35 + 17
2. 46 - 48
3. 117 × 412
4. 144 ÷ 3

At least three of the calculations above could be done easily in one's head. Now try some calculations which would be most difficult, if not impossible, to do in one's head.

5. 39.0123 + 485.18
6. 21.9005 - 1.0098
7. 149.098 × 56.8214
8. 18.0914 ÷ 3.222588

Compare your answers with those at the foot of the next page. No doubt you have correctly computed the results. It was rather easy using the calculator, wasn't it?

The time has now arrived to tackle some more difficult problems. "Difficult" is really the wrong word, because the calculator doesn't have difficulty with any problem. It simply does what it's told to do.

9. $\dfrac{3.73 \times 14.688}{49.01 \times 288.19}$

How would you go about this one? Actually, there are several ways. Here is one of them:

Seq. #	1	2	3	4
Key in	3.73	X	14.688	÷
Display	3.73	3.73	14.688	54.78624

Seq. #	5	6	7	8
Key in	49.01	÷	288.19	=
Display	49.01	1.1178583	288.19	0.0038788

And here is another approach:

Seq. #	1	2	3	4
Key in	3.73	÷	49.01	X
Display	3.73	3.73	49.01	0.0761069

Seq. #	5	6	7	8
Key in	14.688	÷	288.19	=
Display	14.688	1.1178583	288.19	0.0038788

Now let us look at another problem. Suppose you were asked to evaluate the following:

10. $\dfrac{19.683}{20.48} \times \dfrac{89.621}{85.56}$

---

1. 52   2. -2   3. 48204   4. 48
5. 524.1923 6. 20.8907 7. 8466.3886 8. 5.6139351

Without resorting to the calculator, would you accept a result of about 1000, or 100, or 10? You might well shrug your shoulders and claim you have absolutely no idea. But a closer look at the problem will give you a very good idea of the result. The first term

$$\frac{19.683}{20.48}$$

is obviously a little under 1. The second term

$$\frac{89.621}{85.56}$$

is obviously a little over 1. Therefore, the product of the two terms must be about 1. Let us now use the calculator to confirm this "guesstimate."

Seq. #	1	2	3	4
Key in	19.683 ÷		20.48 X	
Display	19.683	19.683	20.48	0.9610839

Seq. #	5	6	7	8
Key in	89.621 ÷		85.56 =	
Display	89.621	86.133307	85.56	1.0067006

Thus, we see that the answer is indeed close to 1. In other words, a rough check without a calculator can often help you to arrive at an approximation of the result, enabling you to reject outright certain incorrect answers. It is extremely easy to key in wrong numbers, and so far no way has been found to prevent this kind of error.

Here are some more arithmetic problems like the ones just discussed. Without resorting to the calculator, check off the best approximation for each one. When you have done all five, use the calculator to find the exact answers, which are listed at the bottom of the page.

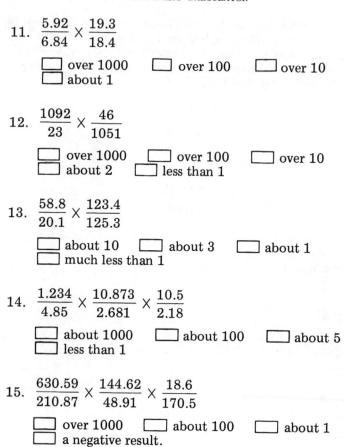

11. $\dfrac{5.92}{6.84} \times \dfrac{19.3}{18.4}$

    ☐ over 1000   ☐ over 100   ☐ over 10
    ☐ about 1

12. $\dfrac{1092}{23} \times \dfrac{46}{1051}$

    ☐ over 1000   ☐ over 100   ☐ over 10
    ☐ about 2   ☐ less than 1

13. $\dfrac{58.8}{20.1} \times \dfrac{123.4}{125.3}$

    ☐ about 10   ☐ about 3   ☐ about 1
    ☐ much less than 1

14. $\dfrac{1.234}{4.85} \times \dfrac{10.873}{2.681} \times \dfrac{10.5}{2.18}$

    ☐ about 1000   ☐ about 100   ☐ about 5
    ☐ less than 1

15. $\dfrac{630.59}{210.87} \times \dfrac{144.62}{48.91} \times \dfrac{18.6}{170.5}$

    ☐ over 1000   ☐ about 100   ☐ about 1
    ☐ a negative result.

2.1 THE PERCENTAGE KEY

All through life, in school, in business, and in the professions, we are interested in calculating the extremely useful statistic called "percentage." *Percent* means literally "per

---

11. 0.9078311   12. 2.0780208   13. 2.8810138
14. 4.970027   15. 0.9646094

100." If 17 of the students in a class of 30 are girls, we say that

$$\frac{17}{30} \times 100$$

or 56.67% are girls. Similarly, the percentage of boys is given by

$$\frac{13}{30} \times 100,$$

which is 43.33%. (Notice that even the sign for percent (%) closely resembles the number 100.)

One can always find the percentage equivalent of a fraction by dividing out the fraction—i.e., dividing the numerator by the denominator—and multiplying by 100. Calculate the following percentages, rounded to two decimal places:

16. $\dfrac{3}{4}$

17. $\dfrac{16}{19}$

18. $\dfrac{1}{7}$

19. $\dfrac{43}{20}$

20. $\dfrac{163}{412}$

---

16. 75%   **17.** 84.21%   **18.** 14.29%

19. 215%   **20.** 39.56%

Percentages are of particular interest when January rolls around. Most big department stores have what are called "white sales." Sheets and linens and other items are then sold at a price considerably lower than the regular price. If an item formerly cost, for example, $5.00 and it is offered at a 35% reduction, it means that we pay $5.00 less 35¢ for each dollar of the cost. That is to say, we save ourselves 5 × 35¢, which is $1.75. Here is how this and similar problems can be solved using the percentage key which is available on the Casio Pocket-Mini and many other calculators.

21. Calculate the cost of a $5.00 item which is reduced by 35%.

Seq. #	1	2	3	4	5
Key in	5	×	35	%	–
Display	5.	5.	35.	1.75	3.25

In step 4, we see that our saving is $1.75, and when this is subtracted from $5.00, we are left with $3.25, the actual cost.

Suppose your calculator does not have a percentage key, just the four standard arithmetic functions. Here is a way to arrive at the same answer, although it means writing down an intermediate result which has to be keyed in subsequently.

Seq. #	1	2	3	4	5
Key in	35	÷	100	×	5
Display	35.	35.	100.	0.35	5.

Seq. #	6	Write down this	7	8	9	10
Key in	=	result for entering	5	–	1.75	=
Display	1.75	in step 9.	5.	5.	1.75	3.25

There are several other ways of arriving at the correct answer. You might be interested in experimenting with your own calculator and trying to find the most efficient method.

22. In a "back-to-school" sale, notebooks are reduced 15%. If the regular price of a set of notebooks was $8.75, how much is the sale price?

Seq. #	1	2	3	4	5
Key in	8.75	X	15	%	–
Display	8.75	8.75	15.	1.3125	7.4375

Thus, we see that the discount amounts to $1.31, reducing the regular price of $8.75 to $7.44.

In the last two examples, the pressing of the percentage key was followed by the minus key in order to calculate the final price. In the next two problems, the discount will again be computed, but then a sales tax will be added.

23. A typewriter regularly selling for $125 is on sale at a 12% discount. If the sales tax is 8% what is the purchase price?

Seq. #	1	2	3	4	5
Key in	125	X	12	%	–
Display	125.	125.	12.	15.	110.

Seq. #	6	7	8	9
Key in	X	8	%	+
Display	110.	8.	8.8	118.8

Thus, we find that the original price of $125 is reduced by 12% to $110. The 8% sales tax of $8.80 is then added, giving a total sales price of $118.80.

24. A retailer buys a gross of pens at $112 per gross. He wants to sell them at a 22% markup. How much must he charge for *each* pen?

Seq. #	1	2	3	4
Key in	112	X	22	%
Display	112.	112.	22.	24.64

Seq. #	5	6	7	8
Key in	+	÷	144	=
Display	136.64	136.64	144.	.9488888

From the above, we see that the retailer would have to sell each pen at 95¢.

So much for the percentage key. Now let us direct our attention to a feature which is invisible to anyone merely looking at a calculator. It is a feature which can be of extreme value for certain problems. It is called a *constant*.

2.2   THE CONSTANT

The Casio Pocket-Mini has an automatic constant on each of the four arithmetic functions. This means that every time an arithmetic operation is performed, the operator (+, -, X, or ÷) and the second operand—i.e., the second number used—are stored in a special register within the calculator for future use. For example, if we multiply 2 by 3, hitting the equals key will display the result of 6. At the same time, the operator "times" and the second operand 3 are both stored, so that if now we want to multiply 4 by 3, all that is necessary is to key in 4 and then press the equals key. The display will automatically show the result of 12, even though we entered only the first part of the expression. The same principle applies for addition, subtraction, and division, as will be seen shortly.

Unfortunately, there is no consistency among calculator manufacturers with respect to the implementation of the constant. First of all, not every calculator has a constant feature. Some that do have a switch which must be turned on before the constant becomes operative. Some calculators have a constant on multiplication and division but not on addition and subtraction. To add to the confusion, some calculators use the first operand for the multiplication constant and the second operand for the division constant. To check the method, if any, with which a calculator operates is very easy. You can either try it out or read the instruction manual.

One of the convenient features of a calculator with a constant is that one can set up an automatic counter very easily. To start counting from 1, 1 is keyed in. Then the plus key is pressed. Now, each time the equals key is pressed, the display is automatically incremented by 1. There are all kinds of situations where an automatic counter of this type can be most useful.

To count from any specific number, key it into the display and add 1. Once again, each time the equals key is pressed, the counter will be incremented by 1 from the initial number.

Can you think of a way to make the calculator count *down* by 1's from a given number? Can you suggest the reason why the counting procedure works?

2.3   RECIPROCALS

The reciprocal of a number is simply 1 divided by that number. For example, the reciprocal of 4 is $\frac{1}{4}$, or .25 in decimal notation. The reciprocal of $\frac{3}{4}$ is

$$\frac{1}{\frac{3}{4}},$$

which is equal to $\frac{4}{3}$, the inverse of the original number.

Most of the basic calculators do not have a reciprocal key. Nevertheless, if there is a division constant which operates on the second operand, it is very easy to find reciprocals. First, key in the number; then press the divide key. Now hit the equals key twice in succession, and the reciprocal will be displayed. The reason why this works can be seen in the following illustrative example.

25.   Calculate the reciprocal of 6, using the constant feature.

Seq. #   1
Key in   6   6 enters the X-register.
Display   6.

Seq. #   2
Key in   ÷   6 enters the Y-register.
Display   6.

Seq. #   3   The contents of the Y-register di-
Key in   =   vided by the contents of the X-regis-
Display   1.   ter, giving the result of 1 and leaving
             ÷ 6 as the constant.

Seq. #   4   Pressing the equals key the second
Key in   =   time causes the constant to operate
Display   0.1666666   on the contents of the X-register,
             giving 1 ÷ 6 = 0.1666666.

2.4 CALCULATING THE SQUARE ROOT

For those calculators with a square root feature, finding
the square root of a number requires no more talent than
keying in that number and pressing the square root key.

In high school, one is generally exposed to a somewhat
unusual method of calculating the square root of a number, involving the pairing off of the digits from right to
left. However, with the modern pocket calculator, one can
take advantage of a method which is generally ascribed to
that great mathematician and physicist Sir Isaac Newton.
This method is used even today for calculating square
roots in modern computers. In essence, the method is
initiated by a guess at the square root of a number. Whatever the guess is, a better guess is then calculated by the
formula

$$\text{new guess} = \frac{1}{2}\left(\frac{x}{\text{old guess}} + \text{old guess}\right),$$

where x is the number whose square root we wish to find. Suppose, for example, we want to find $\sqrt{144}$. (Pretend that we don't know that the square root of 144 is 12.) Let us guess initially that its square root is 1. The new guess is then obtained by evaluating

$$\text{new guess} = \frac{1}{2}\left(\frac{144}{1} + 1\right) = 72.500.$$

This value of 72.5, the new guess, is now substituted back into the formula as the old guess. Thus,

$$\text{new guess} = \frac{1}{2}\left(\frac{144}{72.5} + 72.5\right) = 37.243.$$

This process is repeated as often as is necessary, giving the following sequence of results, rounded to three decimal places.

20.555
13.780
12.115
12.001
12.000
12.000

When there is no change between two successive results, we have found the square root of the number. The closer the first guess is to the correct square root, the quicker this method, sometimes referred to as the Newton-Raphson Iteration Scheme, "converges" to the square root.

The following example shows how an automatic constant may be used when calculating a square root by the Newton-Raphson technique. If your calculator does not have a constant, this sequence will not work. As a challenge, try to develop a sequence that will work with your calculator.

26. Compute $\sqrt{3}$, taking 2 as the initial guess.

Seq. #	1	2	3
Key in	3	÷	2
Display	3.	3.	2.
Comment	x		Initial guess.

Seq. #	4	5	6
Key in	+	2	÷
Display	1.5	2.	3.5

Seq. #	7	8	9
Key in	2	=	÷
Display	2.	1.75	1.75
Comment		Write down this first approximation.	Old guess becomes constant divisor.

Seq. #	10	11	12
Key in	=	3	=
Display	1.	3.	1.7142857
Comment		x	$\dfrac{\text{Old guess}}{x}$

Seq. #	13	14	15
Key in	+	1.75	÷
Display	1.7142857	1.75	3.4642857
Comment		Enter previous approximation.	

Seq. #	16	17	18
Key in	2	=	÷
Display	2.	1.7321428	1.7321428
Comment		Write down this second approximation.	

Seq. #	19	20	21
Key in	=	3	=
Display	1.	3.	1.7319588

Seq. #	22	23	24
Key in	+	1.7321428	÷
Display	1.7319588	1.7321428	3.4641016
Comment		Enter previous approximation.	

Seq. #	25	26	27
Key in	2	=	÷
Display	2.	1.7320508	1.7320508
Comment		Third approximation.	

Seq. #	28	29	30
Key in	=	3	=
Display	1.	3.	1.7320508
Comment			No change from previous approximation, so this is the square root.

At step 30 we find that 3 divided by 1.7320508 gives 1.7320508. Clearly the square root of 3 has been found, and in only the fourth iteration.

2.5 RAISING A NUMBER TO A POSITIVE INTEGER POWER

The multiplication constant can be used to raise a number to a positive integer power. Here is a simple, straightforward way to raise the number 3.14 to the fifth power.

27. Evaluate $(3.14)^5$.

Seq. #	1	2	3
Key in	3.14	×	=
Display	3.14	3.14	9.8596

Seq. #	4	5	6
Key in	=	=	=
Display	30.959144	97.211712	305.24477

Of course, this problem could be solved by successively multiplying out

$$3.14 \times 3.14 \times 3.14 \times 3.14 \times 3.14.$$

However, this is both tedious and unnecessary with a calculator that has a multiplication constant. Generally, to calculate a^n, where n is an integer, key in the following sequence:

$$a \quad \times \underbrace{= = \cdots =}_{n-1 \text{ times}}$$

An extension to this problem is to raise a number to a very large integer power, one which would be extremely tedious, if not intolerable, to calculate. The technique which may be employed is to factor the exponent into its prime factors, e.g., $50 = 25 \times 2 = 2 \times 5 \times 5$. This is the basis for the following sequence, which illustrates a technique for raising the number 1.23 to the 50th power.

28. Evaluate $(1.23)^{50}$.

Seq. #	1	2	3
Key in	1.23	×	=
Display	1.23	1.23	1.5129
Comment			$(1.23)^2$

Seq. #	4	5	6
Key in	×	=	=

Display	1.5129	2.2888664	3.4628259
Comment			

Seq. #	7	8	9
Key in	=	=	×
Display	5.2389093	7.9259458	7.9259458
Comment		$((1.23)^2)^5$	

Seq. #	10	11	12
Key in	=	=	=
Display	62.820616	497.91279	3946.4297
Comment			

Seq. #	13
Key in	=
Display	31279.187
Comment	$(((1.23)^2)^5)^5 = (1.23)^{50}$

The result obtained by this method—31279.187—compares
favorably with the number 31279.19532, which was obtained on the Texas Instruments SR-51 calculator by
raising the number 1.23 to the 50th power using the y^x
key.

The method for raising a number to a negative power is
similar in principle. For example, the expression $(2.34)^{-6}$
may be rewritten in its equivalent form as

$$\frac{1}{(2.34)^6}.$$

To evaluate this expression, first compute the denominator
according to the method suggested above, and then find
the reciprocal according to the method suggested in
section 2.3.

3

The Intermediate Calculator

Early in 1975, National Semiconductor, a large American manufacturer, introduced an interesting new line of pocket calculators at prices ranging between $50 and $70. These new models include the Novus Mathematician, the Scientist, the Statistician, and the Financier. We have selected the Mathematician (model number 4510) for detailed discussion because it possesses some important features which fit logically into our treatment of pocket calculators. What distinguishes the 8-oz. Mathematician from the Casio Pocket-Mini is the fact that it operates not in algebraic logic but rather in so-called reverse Polish notation (RPN), a form of logic used in some of the most elegant and expensive calculators available today. Once an understanding of this calculator is achieved, you will have little difficulty in handling any of the high-powered calculators, even those with price tags as high as $800.

Reverse Polish notation is named after Dr. Jan Lukasciewicz, a Polish mathematician who in 1949 invented a parenthesis-free but unambiguous mathematical language. Over the years this notation has become a standard language of computer science. It is intimately associated with a three or four register stack (to be described shortly), enabling one to solve complex algebraic equations without the need for parentheses or even an equals key. When using RPN, all intermediate answers

are automatically displayed during the course of the calculation. Not only that, but intermediate answers are automatically saved and retrieved as needed. Just in case this sounds unnecessarily complicated, let us assure you that in a very short time you will feel completely at home with this notation. Indeed, there are many calculator owners who will not consider any logic other than reverse Polish notation for their personal pocket calculator.

The Novus Mathematician calculator provides the user with a memory for accumulating sums. Other important features include the trigonometric functions, sine, cosine, tangent, and their inverses, as well as y^x, e^x, ln, $1/x$, π, $\sqrt{x}$, log, X- and Y-register interchange (marked $x \leftrightarrow y$), x^2, a change sign key labelled CHS permitting the entry of negative numbers, and a radian-degrees key.

The picture of the Mathematician on page 34 indicates all of its essential features:

3.1   REVERSE POLISH NOTATION

In reverse Polish notation, the operation to be performed follows the two associated operands. In case this sounds esoteric, all we mean is that when a and b are added, the addition operation follows the operands a and b. This is usually written as $a\ b +$. Using this notation, the slightly more complex expression

$$a + (b \times c)$$

is represented as

$$a\ b\ c \times +.$$

At first glance, this may look strange, but all that it means is that the first operation listed, multiplication, operates on the *two immediately preceding operands*, b and c, reducing them to one number. Then, the next operation, addition, operates on the two preceding quantities, namely a and $b \times c$. Notice that when using this notation, we no longer have to concern ourselves with parentheses, and yet the notation is never ambiguous. Taking a specific example to illustrate this point further,

$$3 + (4 \times 5)$$

is written in RPN as

$$3\ 4\ 5 \times +.$$

Scanning from left to right, we encounter multiplication as the first operation. This operates on the two immediately preceding operands, 4 and 5, reducing them to the single number 20, which gives us

$$3\ 20 +.$$

Next, the addition operator is encountered, and 3 is added to 20, giving the result of 23.

Here is a list of algebraic expressions, some simple and

some not so simple, with their equivalents in reverse Polish notation:

Algebraic Notation	*Reverse Polish Notation*
$a + b$	$a\ b\ +$
$a - b$	$a\ b\ -$
$a \times b$	$a\ b\ \times$
$a \div b$	$a\ b\ \div$
$a + (b \times c)$	$a\ b\ c\ \times\ +$
$a - (b \times c)$	$a\ b\ c\ \times\ -$
$a(b + c)$	$a\ b\ c\ +\ \times$
$\dfrac{a}{b + c}$	$a\ b\ c\ +\ \div$
$a + \dfrac{b}{c}$	$a\ b\ c\ \div\ +$
$a - \dfrac{b}{c}$	$a\ b\ c\ \div\ -$
$(a \times b) + (c \times d)$	$a\ b\ \times\ c\ d\ \times\ +$
$(a + b) \times (c + d)$	$a\ b\ +\ c\ d\ +\ \times$
$a + (b \times (c + d))$	$a\ b\ c\ d\ +\ \times\ +$
$a \times \left(b + \left(\dfrac{c}{d} - e\right)\right)$	$a\ b\ c\ d\ \div\ e\ -\ +\ \times$

Try your hand at converting the following expressions, presented in the familiar algebraic notation, into RPN. The answers are shown at the bottom of the next page.

1. $a + b - c$

2. $\dfrac{a}{b}$

3. $\dfrac{a}{b} + (a + b - c)$

4. $\dfrac{x + y}{a + z}$

5. $\dfrac{u(v + w)}{z + \left(m - \dfrac{n}{p}\right)}$

Before we describe how the stack works on the Mathematician, we will solve some elementary problems in order to acquaint you with the mode of operation.

6. Calculate 2 + 3.

To add 2 and 3, we key in 2 first and "enter" it by pressing the key marked ENT↑. Next, 3 is keyed in, and the sum is calculated by pressing the plus key.

Seq. #	1	2	3	4
Key in	2	ENT↑	3	+
Display	2	2.	3	5.

7. Evaluate $(3 \times 4.6) - 8$.

Seq. #	1	2	3	4	5	6
Key in	3	ENT↑	4.6	×	8	-
Display	3	3.	4.6	13.8	8	5.8

Thus, the answer as calculated on the Mathematician is 5.8.

The reader may be puzzled as to why this strange key sequence produces the correct result. To answer this, we need to explain the operation of the register stack in the Mathematician. The stack may be represented schematically as follows:

Z	
Y	
X	

Each of the three rectangles shown represents a separate register, named X, Y, and Z, respectively. The X-register is simply another name for the display. Referring to ex-

---

1. $a\ b + c -$ 2. $a\ b \div$ 3. $a\ b \div a\ b + c - +$
4. $x\ y + a\ z + \div$ 5. $u\ v\ w + \times z\ m\ n\ p \div - + \div$

ample 1, where we used the calculator to compute 2 + 3, we begin by keying in the first operand, 2. This places 2 in the X-register as shown:

Z	
Y	
X	2

Next, the ENT↑ key is pressed. This has the effect of *copying* the contents of the X-register, 2, into the Y-register, which is immediately adjacent to it. So now, the stack looks like this:

Z	
Y	2
X	2

Now 3 is keyed in, *replacing* 2, which was previously in the X-register. Schematically, this is what has happened:

Z	
Y	2
X	3

Finally, the operation—in this case addition—is initiated by pressing the plus key. At this point the contents of the X- and Y-registers are *automatically* added together, placing the result in the X-register, the display register. The Y-register is automatically cleared.

Z	
Y	
X	5

Admittedly, this does not seem like a very efficient way to add two numbers, but a fuller appreciation of RPN will be obtained after the next few examples. We will now illustrate the operation of the stack in solving problem 7, in which the expression (3 × 4.6) – 8 was evaluated.

(1) 3 is keyed in.

Z	
Y	
X	3

(2) The ENT↑ key is pressed.

Z	
Y	3
X	3

(3) 4.6 is keyed in.

Z	
Y	3
X	4.6

(4) The times key is pressed.

Z	
Y	
X	13.8	(3 × 4.6)

(5) 8 is keyed in.
Note: At this point, keying in a new number into the X-register will push up whatever number was there previously. Thus, 13.8, which was in the X-register, is transmitted to the Y-register when 8 is keyed in.

Z	
Y	13.8
X	8

(6) The minus button is pressed, subtracting the X-register from the Y-register.

Z		
Y		
X	5.8	(13.8 – 8)

The reason why the ENT↑ key has an upward arrow alongside it is to remind you that every time a number is ENTered, the stack is pushed upwards. Whenever the stack is pushed upwards, the contents of the Z-register is lost.

In order to thoroughly familiarize you with the way the stack of registers works, here is a somewhat more involved example:

8. Evaluate $(6.12 - 4.01) + (1.23 \times 6.5) \div (\frac{1}{2.5} + 9.8)$.

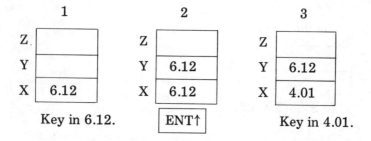

	1		2		3
Z		Z		Z	
Y		Y	6.12	Y	6.12
X	6.12	X	6.12	X	4.01
	Key in 6.12.		ENT↑		Key in 4.01.

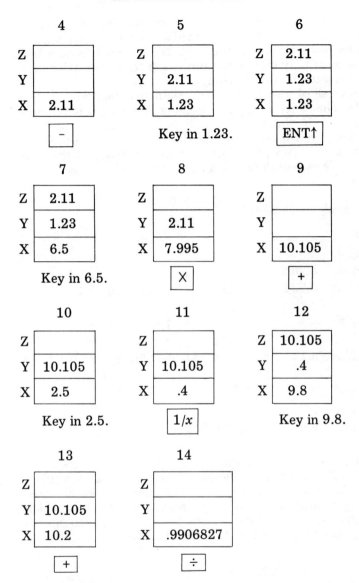

4

Z	
Y	
X	2.11

[−]

5

Z	
Y	2.11
X	1.23

Key in 1.23.

6

Z	2.11
Y	1.23
X	1.23

[ENT↑]

7

Z	2.11
Y	1.23
X	6.5

Key in 6.5.

8

Z	
Y	2.11
X	7.995

[×]

9

Z	
Y	
X	10.105

[+]

10

Z	
Y	10.105
X	2.5

Key in 2.5.

11

Z	
Y	10.105
X	.4

[1/x]

12

Z	10.105
Y	.4
X	9.8

Key in 9.8.

13

Z	
Y	10.105
X	10.2

[+]

14

Z	
Y	
X	.9906827

[÷]

On the surface it would seem as though we have gone to an awful lot of trouble to calculate a solution which we could have done easily with a less sophisticated calculator.

With the Mathematician, however, we did not have to write down a single intermediate answer; instead, we stored each of them in the stack of registers. It is clear that you must fully understand how these registers work before you can use them effectively.

Several of the keys of the Mathematician have a dual role. The function name appearing above a key is available directly. If there is a function name below a key (in yellow), you must first press the yellow F key before you can use it. This procedure becomes necessary in the next example, where the x^2 function is required.

9. Evaluate $(5.234)^2 - \dfrac{(3.14 \times 62.98)}{81.6}$

Seq. #	1	2	3	4
Key in	5.234	F	x^2	3.14
Display	5.234	5.234	27.394756	3.14

Seq. #	5	6	7	8
Key in	ENT↑	62.98	×	81.6
Display	3.14	62.98	197.7572	81.6

Seq. #	9	10
Key in	÷	–
Display	2.423495	24.971261

With this we conclude our introductory discussion of RPN. The additional functions found on the intermediate calculator will be covered in later chapters. We are now ready to move on to the super-scientific calculator, which contains a great number of new functions not encountered on either of the machines described so far.

4

The Advanced Calculator

Courses in advanced mathematics, physics, and chemistry demand a high level of mathematical skill and computational ability. Not only are students expected to be completely at home with scientific notation, they also have to be proficient in trigonometry, geometry, algebra, and even a limited amount of statistics. For students who are taking, or who plan to take, such courses, there is a variety of scientific and advanced scientific calculators available. We have selected as representative of this type of calculator the Texas Instruments SR-51, which may currently be bought for well under $100 in certain discount stores. Before introducing the advanced calculator, however, we will briefly review the principles of scientific notation.

4.1 SCIENTIFIC NOTATION

The number 12.34 is written in the standard decimal form. However, it is capable of being expressed in another standardized form known as scientific notation. For example, the number 12.34 may also be written

$$1.234 \times 10^1$$
$$\text{or} \quad 0.1234 \times 10^2$$
$$\text{or} \quad 0.01234 \times 10^3$$
$$\text{etc.}$$

It could also be represented as

$$123.4 \times 10^{-1}$$
$$\text{or} \quad 1234. \times 10^{-2}$$
$$\text{or} \quad 12340. \times 10^{-3}$$
$$\text{etc.}$$

The specific resistance (resistivity) of mercury at $0°C$ is 9.407×10^{-5}, according to a standard physics textbook. Another way of writing this number is 0.00009407, but in using the number in this form there is a great possibility of miscounting the number of zeros. Think how much more prone to error a number such as 0.00000000000004123 would be. It would be much safer to write it in scientific notation as 4.123×10^{-14}, where the exponent -14 indicates that the decimal point should be moved 14 places to the *left*. Similarly, -12345600000000 would be easier to handle if it were written -1.23456×10^{13}, where the exponent 13 means that the decimal point should be moved 13 places to the *right*.

The first part of a number written in scientific notation is called the *mantissa*; the power to which the base 10 is raised is the *exponent*. Note that both the mantissa and the exponent may take a negative sign. If they are positive, the plus sign is generally omitted. It is conventional to write the mantissa with one nonzero digit to the left of the decimal point. The exponent never takes a decimal point. It serves to indicate how many places to the left or right the decimal point in the mantissa must be moved.

Suppose we had no calculator—just pencil and paper—and we wanted to multiply 2.5 million by 234. It could be done like this:

$$
\begin{array}{r}
2\,500\,000 \\
\times\,234 \\
\hline
500\,000\,000 \\
75\,000\,000 \\
10\,000\,000 \\
\hline
585\,000\,000
\end{array}
$$

The result of 585 million is, of course, quite correct, but in point of fact all that was used of the first number was the first two digits, i.e., 25. The string of zeros is irrelevant, confusing, and risky to use, since the omission of one of them—or the inclusion of an additional one—could result in an entirely inaccurate answer.

Suppose, however, we were to write 2,500,000 in scientific notation with a mantissa of 2.5 and an exponent of 6. The calculation now becomes

$$
\begin{array}{r}
2.5 \quad (\times 10^6) \\
234 \\
\hline
100 \\
750 \\
5000 \\
\hline
585.0 \quad (\times 10^6)
\end{array}
$$

The result of 585.0 has to be multiplied by 10^6 to arrive at the conventional form; this is done by moving the decimal point to the right six places:

$$585.000000 \longrightarrow 585\ 000\ 000$$

The number 234 can also be expressed in scientific notation as 2.34×10^2. In this case, our problem can be written

$$
\begin{array}{r}
2.5 \quad \times 10^6 \\
2.34 \quad \times 10^2 \\
\hline
100 \\
750 \\
5000 \\
\hline
5.850 \quad \times 10^8
\end{array}
$$

where the exponent of the answer is 8, which is obtained by *adding* the exponents of the two operands.

So much for scientific notation. We will now briefly turn our attention to the type of calculator which has a keyboard crammed full with scientific functions and which has the ability to accept and display numbers in scientific notation.

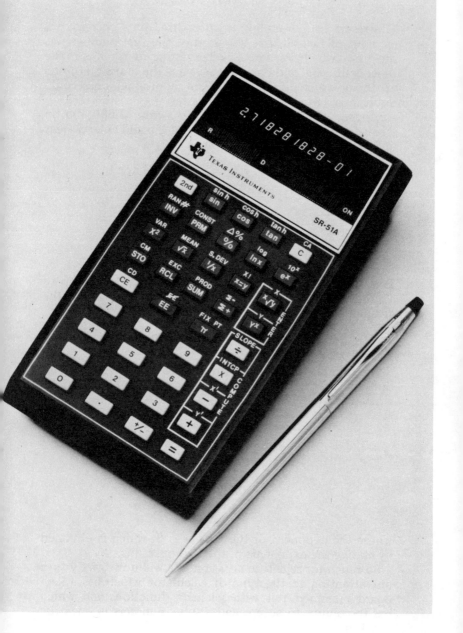

4.2 THE SR-51

Unlike both of the calculators previously described, the Texas Instruments SR-51, which incidentally uses a modified algebraic logic, is capable of handling scientific notation and can calculate results to 13 significant digits, even though only 10 (rounded) are displayed. It is also capable of storing numbers in three different "addressable" memory locations; of calculating all of the trigonometric (including hyperbolic) and logarithmic functions together with their inverses; and of providing a host of other useful scientific and statistical functions, such as random numbers, x^2, $\sqrt{x}$, $1/x$, standard deviation, mean, variance, y^x, $x!$, etc.

Since a detailed description of the SR-51 or its later version, the SR-51A, would require many pages to do it justice, we will confine ourselves to those features which will actually be used in solving the problems found in later chapters. A picture of the SR-51A appears on page 46. A glance will give you an idea of its sophistication, but the full extent of its calculating power will only become apparent when we begin to use it to solve complex problems.

5
Going Metric

If you have been driving recently along the highways of Ohio or of Long Island, New York, you might have noticed that some of the road signs display distances in both miles and kilometers. If you drive a Ford Pinto, you might be surprised to know that the engine is built to metric specifications. IBM now designs all of its engineering projects in both the standard American units and the decimal units of the metric system. What's more, it has been doing so since 1966. You can also see metric measurements in the advertisements that point out the virtues of the 100-millimeter cigarette, or more recently, the 120-mm cigarette. Conversions to the metric system are also underway in the soft drink industry, the wine industry, the canning industry, and many others.

In some areas we have been using the metric system for a long time. Medical prescriptions have traditionally been written in metric units, and camera buffs are quite at home dealing with film sizes specified in metric units. Those with 20/20 vision might be surprised to know that this designation is based on metric measurements.

On February 15, 1971, the United Kingdom converted from their long-standing pounds, shillings, and pence to a decimal currency. Considering that they had been using their original system of 12 pence to the shilling and 20 shillings to the pound for no less than 1,200 years, the conversion represented a dramatic change.

Our neighbors to the north (the Canadians) began an irreversible step towards "metrication" or "metrification," early in 1975. Within five years gasoline will be bought in liters and food in grams and kilograms; road signs will indicate kilometers. This is not only in the French-speaking provinces, but in all of Canada.

In the United States there is not yet any official program compelling the nation to go metric, but the idea has been broached on numerous occasions. As far back as 1866, Congress passed an act permitting the use of the metric system in the United States. In 1968, the government undertook a three-year study of the impact of the increasing worldwide use of the metric system. The result of this study was a report entitled "A Metric America—A Decision Whose Time Has Come."

The metrication bills which are submitted to Congress are appropriately named. The Senate bill is designated Senate 100, while the House of Representatives bill is called H.R. 254. Just in case you are wondering about the number 254, it was selected because there are 2.54 centimeters to the inch!

It is clear that despite the expense and inconvenience involved, the United States is going to be forced to go metric because most of the world is already using this system. Sooner or later, all of us are going to have to deal with metric conversions whether we like it or not. The schools are not waiting for Congress to act. They are already teaching the metric system in the early grades because it seems quite obvious that by the time these children enter college, the metric system will be firmly established, and our archaic system of weights and measures will be but a faint memory. The schools in California, New Jersey, and Maryland are formally committed to the metric system beginning in 1976; other states are bound to follow suit.

Calculators have already been introduced which are designed for conversion to metric units. We feel that even the basic four-function calculator, however, is sufficient for most work on metrication. In the chapters that follow, we will illustrate several methods of converting standard American units to metric units on the various calculators.

If you are interested in receiving free materials on this important subject, write to

National Bureau of Standards
Washington, D.C. 20234

Upon request, they will send you a pamphlet on the history of metrication, a special color publication (#304A), a plasticized ruler and card, conversion tables, and references to associated information.

5.1 TABLES OF EQUIVALENCE

The following prefixes are widely used in the metric system:

kilo-	means	1000
hecto-	means	100
deka-	means	10
deci-	means	$\frac{1}{10}$
centi-	means	$\frac{1}{100}$
milli-	means	$\frac{1}{1000}$

You can see how these prefixes are used in the following table, which shows how the metric units of length are related to each other.

10 millimeters (mm)	= 1 centimeter (cm)
10 centimeters	= 1 decimeter (dm) = 100 mm
10 decimeters	= 1 meter (m) = 1000 mm
10 meters	= 1 dekameter (dam)
10 dekameters	= 1 hectometer (hm) = 100 meters
10 hectometers	= 1 kilometer (km) = 1000 meters

Length

1 cm = 0.3937 in	1 in	= 2.5400 cm
1 m = 3.2808 ft	1 ft	= 0.3048 m
1 m = 1.0936 yd	1 yd	= 0.9144 m
1 km = 0.6214 mile	1 mile	= 1.6093 km

```
1 fathom = 6 ft     = 1.8288 m
1 furlong = 660 ft  = 220 yd    = 201.168 m
1 mile    = 5280 ft = 1760 yd
```

Area

1 sq cm	= 0.1550 sq in	1 sq in	= 6.4516 sq cm
1 sq m	= 10.7639 sq ft	1 sq ft	= 0.0929 sq m
1 sq m	= 1.1960 sq yd	1 sq yd	= 0.8361 sq m
1 hectare	= 2.4710 acres	1 acre	= 0.4047 hectares
1 sq km	= 0.3861 sq mile	1 sq mile	= 2.5900 sq km

```
1 acre    = 43,560 sq ft = 4,840 sq yd
1 sq cm   = 0.155 sq in
1 sq ft   = 929.030 sq cm
1 sq mile = 258.999 hectares
1 sq mm   = 0.002 sq in
```

Volume or Capacity

1 cu cm	= 0.0610 cu in	1 cu in	= 16.3872 cu cm
1 cu m	= 35.3145 cu ft	1 cu ft	= 0.0283 cu m
1 cu m	= 1.3079 cu yd	1 cu yd	= 0.7646 cu m

```
1 cu ft  = 7.481 gal   = 28.316 cu dm
1 cu in  = 0.554 fl oz = 4.433 fl drams
1 cu yd  = 0.765 cu m
```

```
1 US gal   = 231 cu in      = 3.7853 liters = 0.833 British gal
1 liter (l) = 1.057 liq qt  = 0.908 dry qt = 61.0250 cu in
1 peck     = 8.810 l
1 pt       = 33.600 cu in = 0.551 l
```

1 l = 0.0353 cu ft	1 cu ft	= 28.3162 l
1 l = 0.2642 US gal	1 gal	= 3.7853 l
1 l = 0.0284 US bushel	1 bushel	= 35.2383 l
1 l = 1000.027 cu cm	1 liter	= 2.2046 lb of pure water

Weight

1 gram (g)	= 15.4324 grains	1 grain	= 0.0648 g
1 g	= 0.0353 oz	1 oz	= 28.3495 g
1 kilogram (kg)	= 2.2046 lb	1 lb	= 0.4536 kg

6

The System to Be Used in This Book

In the following chapters we will show how different kinds of problems may be solved, in most cases using each of the three types of calculators. The solution using the basic calculator will be indicated by A, that using the intermediate calculator by B, and that using the advanced calculator by C. Where necessary, explanations will be given and appropriate comments made.

You are encouraged to follow the examples and to work through the exercises, using whichever calculator is available to you. Answers to the exercises are printed in the appendix, so it will not be difficult to check whether your work is correct or not.

In certain cases, your result may be slightly different from the one given in this book. This could easily be due to your calculator's being more or less accurate than ours. Any discrepancy is likely to be in the sixth or seventh decimal place, so that usually it will not be particularly bothersome.

Since we assume that most students will own a basic calculator, the bulk of the problems given can be solved using nothing more sophisticated than the standard four-function calculator—the so-called four-banger. In the more advanced problems, the more specialized and correspondingly more expensive calculators will be seen to solve the problems more elegantly, with many fewer steps and usually with a greater degree of accuracy.

6.1 SOME FUNDAMENTAL CONCEPTS

A *term* is an algebraic expression representing a single quantity. For example,

$$3a + \frac{4b}{c} - 5d^2$$

is an expression of three terms.

The result of an addition is the *sum*. The result of a subtraction is the *difference*. When two numbers are multiplied together, the result is the *product*, while if one number is divided by another, the result is called the *quotient*. Whereas implied multiplication is perfectly valid in algebra, the multiplication operation must, of necessity, be performed explicitly on a calculator. For example, in the equation $y = ab$, you understand that the a is to be *multiplied* by b, whereas the calculator must be told explicitly to multiply—$y = a \times b$.

6.2 ORDER OF OPERATIONS

Whenever an expression is to be evaluated, the multiplications and divisions are done first, in left-to-right order. Once they have been completed, the additions and subtractions are performed again from left to right.

To alter the order in which terms are calculated, one may resort to parentheses. Placing parentheses around two or more expressions causes them to be considered as a single quantity.

6.3 OVERFLOW AND UNDERFLOW

When the result of a calculation produces a number which exceeds the maximum capacity of the display of the calculator, "overflow" is said to have occurred. Usually, the calculator has a special means of notifying the user that overflow has indeed taken place. This may involve a flashing display, the activation of a special overflow light, either inside or outside of the regular display panel, or the presence of all zeros in the display, depending upon the calculator. Some calculators do not provide for any indication at all when overflow occurs. Some of those that do lock the keyboard automatically, preventing further calculations until the clear button is pressed.

Overflow may be caused by any of the following:

(1) multiplying two numbers whose product overflows the capacity of the display
(2) dividing a relatively large number by a small number
(3) dividing by zero
(4) adding two numbers whose sum exceeds the display's capacity
(5) taking the tangent of 90°
(6) taking the inverse sine and cosine trigonometric functions of numbers greater than 1
(7) taking the square root or logarithm of a negative number
(8) raising a negative number or zero to a power

When the result of a calculation produces a number which is too small to represent in the display, "underflow" is said to have occurred. Some calculators have a special indicator to advise the user that underflow has taken place, whereas other calculators treat the result as zero, permitting continued operation.

Underflow may be caused by any of the following:

(1) multiplying two relatively small numbers, both of which are less than 1
(2) dividing a very small number by a very large number
(3) taking the reciprocal of a very large number

6.4 TRUNCATION AND ROUNDING

In several of the problems we have discussed so far, the result displayed has differed very slightly from the expected result. This is due to the fact that in certain calculations the physical constraints of a calculator introduce slight inaccuracies. For example, the reciprocal of 3 is $\frac{1}{3}$. On an eight-digit calculator it is always displayed as 0.3333333, even though the true representation contains an infinite number of 3's. What is displayed is therefore somewhat less than the true value. Taking the reciprocal of this displayed value for $\frac{1}{3}$ does not return the original 3, as one might expect. This kind of error is known as *truncation*.

When calculating the fraction $\frac{2}{3}$, one generally sees the number 0.6666666 displayed. Once again, this is not the exact answer because it is impossible to display an infinite number of 6's in a calculator. This is also a source of truncation error, but it can be reduced by rounding the last digit. On a few calculators, such as the SR-50, SR-51, HP-21, HP-25, HP-35, HP-45 and HP-65, the rounding is done automatically without loss of significant digits. These are the exceptions rather than the rule.

"Rounding" means adding 1 to the next to last digit if the last digit is 5 or more. So that the rounded fraction for $\frac{2}{3}$ would become 0.6666667.

6.5 THE USEFUL CONSTANT π

The constant *pi*, written with the Greek letter π, is used a great deal in scientific and mathematical work. It occurs in many formulas, including the following:

$$\text{circumference of a circle: } C = 2\pi r$$

$$\text{area of a circle: } A = \pi r^2$$

$$\text{volume of a sphere: } V = \frac{4}{3} \pi r^3$$

$$\text{swing of a pendulum: } T = 2\pi \sqrt{\frac{l}{g}}$$

$$\text{normal distribution: } Y = \frac{1}{2\sqrt{\pi}} e^{-\frac{1}{2} z^2}$$

Two approximate values for the irrational number π are $\frac{22}{7}$ and 3.14159. Some calculators have a π key and give its value to even greater accuracy. A simple way to calculate a close approximation to π is to think of the following sequence:

$$11 \ 33 \ 55$$

Now split this sequence down the middle, giving two numbers 113 and 355. The result of dividing 355 by 113 is displayed as 3.1415929, which is an approximation of π accurate to the sixth decimal place. (The last digit should actually be a 6 rather than a 9.)

A way to remember the value of π to the seventh decimal place is to refer to the phrase "May I have a drink, alcoholic of course." The number of letters in each successive word corresponds to the appropriate digit for π.

7
Algebra

7.1 EVALUATING FORMULAS

1. Evaluate $x = 3a + 4c$, when $a = 5$ and $c = 7$.

Solution:
Note that this problem cannot be solved directly on the basic calculator by keying in

$$3 \times 5 + 4 \times 7.$$

If keyed in this order, the problem would ordinarily be evaluated as

$$((3 \times 5) + 4) \times 7,$$

which gives a result of 133 rather than 43, which is correct. What we actually want to compute is

$$x = (3 \times 5) + (4 \times 7).$$

A	S	1	2	3	4	
	K	3	$\times$	5	=	Write down this partial result.
	D	3.	3.	5.	15.	
	S	5	6	7	8	Now it is necessary to add the
	K	4	$\times$	7	=	partial result 15.
	D	4.	4.	7.	28.	

```
S  9      10    11
K  +      15    =
D  28.    15.   43.
```

```
B  S  1  2        3  4    5  6       7  8    9
   K  3  ENT↑     5  ×    4  ENT↑    7  ×    +
   D  3  3.       5  15.  4  4.      7  28.  43.
```

```
C  S  1  2  3  4    5   6   7  8
   K  3  ×  5  +    4   ×   7  =
   D  3  3.  5  15.  4  4.  7  43.
```

2. Evaluate $y = 2a^2 - 3b^3 + 11.2$, when $a = 2.6$ and $b = 3.2$.

```
A  S  1    2    3    4     5   6      Write down this
   K  2.6  ×    2.6  ×     2   =      result.
   D  2.6  2.6  2.6  6.76  2.  13.52
```

```
S  7    8    9    10     11   12
K  3.2  ×    3.2  ×      3.2  ×
D  3.2  3.2  3.2  10.24  3.2  32.768
```

```
S  13  14      Write down this result and     15
K  3   =       reenter the first inter-        13.52
D  3.  98.304  mediate result from step 6.     13.52
```

```
S  16     17      18        19     20
K  -      98.304  +         11.2   =
D  13.52  98.304  -84.784   11.2   -73.584
```

Thus, in 20 steps we arrive at the result of −73.584, using the basic calculator. For one with a constant on multiplication, the term $(2.6)^2$ could have been obtained by keying in 2.6 and following it with the multiplication key and the equals key. The only gain is that the number would not have had to be keyed in again. Later on, however, when b^3 is calculated, a step could have been saved by resorting to this technique and keying in 3.2, following it with the multiplication key and two hits of the equals key. Since b is raised to the power 3, the equals key is pressed $n - 1$, or 2 times.

Another point worth mentioning is that it is not strictly necessary to write down the intermediate result at step 14. It is possible to subtract a displayed value for a subsequent entry by converting the displayed number into a constant subtraction factor. This may be done by keying in the following sequence:

$$- \quad = \quad \text{enter number} \quad =$$

Each of these improvements has been included in the revised sequence which follows.

A	S	1	2	3	4
	K	2.6	X	=	X
	D	2.6	2.6	6.76	6.76

	S	5	6	Write down	7
	K	2	=	this result.	3.2
	D	2.	13.52		3.2

	S	8	9	10	11
	K	X	=	=	X
	D	3.2	10.24	32.768	32.768

	S	12	13	14	15
	K	3	-	=	13.52
	D	3.	98.304	0.	13.52

	S	16	17	18	19
	K	=	+	11.2	=
	D	-84.784	-84.784	11.2	-73.584

Even though this revised sequence achieves the same result in 19 instead of 20 steps, it might seem to you that in view of the complexity involved, it was not worth the trouble. This might indeed be the case in this particular example. In other situations, however, resorting to these kinds of techniques can be of considerable help. If you are not sure of these techniques, however, you should avoid them and stick to the straight order of operations. The major benefit achieved in the above example was that we avoided having to write down one intermediate result. This proves to be an asset, since one of the major sources of error when using calculators is the incorrect copying down and reentering of intermediate results. In the long run, not having to write down intermediate results also saves time. These techniques are not necessary with the more sophisticated calculators, as will be seen in the next two sequences.

B	S	1	2	3	4	5
	K	2.6	F	x^2	2	$\times$
	D	2.6	2.6	6.76	2	13.52
	S	6	7	8	9	10
	K	3.2	ENT↑	$\times$	3.2	$\times$
	D	3.2	3.2	10.24	3.2	32.768
	S	11	12	13	14	15
	K	3	$\times$	$-$	11.2	$+$
	D	3	98.304	-84.784	11.2	-73.584

Thus, we find that by using the intermediate level calculator we arrive at the same result in 15 steps. Perhaps it should be pointed out that the method used for evaluating this expression is only one of several approaches that could have been taken.

Before suggesting a method for evaluating this expression on the SR-51, there are several features regarding its logic which should be made clear. Calculations involving a chain sequence of multiplication, division, addition, and subtraction on the SR-51 are treated in exactly the same way that they are in algebra. That is to say, *multiplication and division are given priority over addition and subtraction.* In other words, the key sequence

$$3 + 4 \times 5$$

is evaluated as $3 + (4 \times 5)$ and *not* as $(3 + 4) \times 5$, as is the case on many other algebraic logic calculators. Similarly, the sequence

$$4 + 10 \div 5$$

produces a result of 6 on the SR-51 $(4 + 2)$, indicating that the division is done prior to the addition. This somewhat unique feature enables the sum of the products

$$(a \times b) + (c \times d)$$

to be evaluated directly on the SR-51, and in precisely the same order as the expression is written. This applies equally to the SR-50 calculator, and it is quite likely that in the future more models will behave in this way.

The other feature of the SR-51 which we would like to emphasize concerns the y^x key, which raises a number y to a power x. To raise 2 to the power 3, that is to say 2^3, one keys in the sequence

$$2 \quad y^x \quad 3 \quad =,$$

which yields the correct result of 8. However, the sequence

$$3 \quad \times \quad 5 \quad y^x \quad 4 \quad =$$

calculates $(3 \times 5)^4$ rather than 3×5^4, which one might mistakenly think. What this means is that, in effect, the pressing of the y^x key completes any unevaluated multiplications or divisions, just as if the equals key had been pressed. The sequence

$$3 \quad + \quad 5 \quad y^x \quad 4$$

will, however, calculate $3 + 5^4$, as one ordinarily expects, and similarly for

$$3 \quad - \quad 5 \quad y^x \quad 4.$$

If you bear the above in mind, the following sequence, which solves the problem in only 13 steps, will be more meaningful.

C	S	1	2	3	4	5	6	7
	K	2	×	2.6	x^2	–	3.2	y^x
	D	2	2.	2.6	6.76	13.52	3.2	3.2

	S	8	9	10	11	12	13
	K	3	×	3	+	11.2	=
	D	3	32.768	3	-84.784	11.2	-73.584

7.2 EXERCISES

Evaluate the following expressions on your calculator. The answers can be found in the Appendix.

1. $(3.58 + 29.76) \times (88.72 - 36.54)$

2. $\dfrac{5.86}{6.78 + 39.74}$

3. $V = \frac{4}{3}\pi r^3$, where $r = 1.987$ and $\pi = 3.1416$

4. $S = \frac{1}{2}gt^2$, where $g = 32$ and $t =$ (a) 5.09
    (b) 2.1
    (c) 39.685

5. $A = \pi r^2$, where $r =$ (a) 3
    (b) 2.987
    (c) 39.685

6. $A = p + prt$, where (a) $p = 500$, $r = .02$, $t = 2$
    (b) $p = 358.75$, $r = 0.65$, $t = .35$

7. $S = 2\pi r(r + l)$, where $\pi = 3.1416$, $r = 49.87$, and
$$l = 26.3215$$

8. $H = \dfrac{DV}{375}$, where $D = 187.58$ and $V = 48.369$

9. $F = \frac{9}{5}(C + 32)$, where $C = $ (a) 0
(b) − 40
(c) 98.7

10. $S = \dfrac{n}{2}(a + l)$; find n where $S = 30$, $a = 4$, and $l = 6$.

7.3   ANGULAR MEASUREMENT

The following exercises deal with angles measured in degrees. You will recall, no doubt, that there are $360°$ in a circle. Also, an angle is said to be *supplementary* to another angle if their sum is $180°$.

3. If two supplementary angles are in the ratio of $1:6$, find the number of degrees in the measure of the smaller angle, to the nearest tenth of a degree.

Solution:
Since the angles are in the ratio of $1:6$, it follows that if the smaller of the two angles is x degrees, the larger one is $6x$ degrees. Since the two angles are supplementary, their sum,

$$x + 6x = 7x,$$

is equal to $180°$. Therefore,

$$7x = 180$$
$$x = \frac{180}{7}$$

A	S	1	2	3	4
	K	180	÷	7	=
	D	180.	180.	7.	25.714285

B	S	1	2	3	4
	K	180	ENT↑	7	÷
	D	180	180.	7	25.714285

C	S	1	2	3	4
	K	180	÷	7	=
	D	180	180.	7	25.71428571

Thus, we have found the smaller angle to be 25.7°, to the nearest tenth.

To Check:

$$x + 6x = 180, \text{ where } x \approx 25.7$$

A	S	1	2	3	4	5	6
	K	25.7	✕	6	+	25.7	=
	D	25.7	25.7	6.	154.2	25.7	179.9

B	S	1	2	3	4	5	6
	K	25.7	ENT↑	6	✕	25.7	+
	D	25.7	25.7	6	154.2	25.7	179.9

C	S	1	2	3	4	5	6
	K	25.7	+	6	✕	25.7	=
	D	25.7	25.7	6	6.	25.7	179.9

4. The sum of the measures of two angles is 90°. If one angle is three times the other, find the number of degrees in the smaller of the two angles.

   Solution:
   If we let the smaller of the two angles be x degrees, then it follows that $3x$ represents the number of degrees in the larger angle. Since the sum of the two angles is 90°, we have

$$x + 3x = 90$$
$$4x = 90$$
$$x = \frac{90}{4}$$

A	S	1	2	3	4
	K	90	÷	4	=
	D	90.	90.	4.	22.5

B	S	1	2	3	4
	K	90	ENT↑	4	÷
	D	90	90.	4	22.5

C	S	1	2	3	4
	K	90	÷	4	=
	D	90	90.	4	22.5

Thus, we have found that the measure of the smaller of the two angles is 22.5°.

To Check:

$$x + 3x = 90, \text{ where } x = 22.5$$

A	S	1	2	3	4	5	6
	K	3	×	22.5	+	22.5	=
	D	3.	3.	22.5	67.5	22.5	90.

B	S	1	2	3	4	5	6
	K	22.5	ENT↑	ENT↑	3	×	+
	D	22.5	22.5	22.5	3	67.5	90.

C	S	1	2	3	4	5	6
	K	22.5	+	3	×	22.5	=
	D	22.5	22.5	3	3	22.5	90.

7.4   AREA PROBLEMS

5. The length of a rectangle exceeds its width by 3 inches. If the area of the rectangle is 40 square inches, find the measure of its length and width.

Solution:

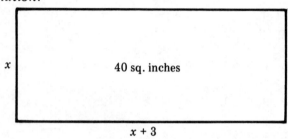

$$x + 3$$

Let x = width of the rectangle. Then $x + 3$ = the length of the rectangle. The area of a rectangle equals the product of its length and width or

$$\text{area} = \text{length} \times \text{width}$$
$$40 = (x + 3) \times x$$
$$40 = x^2 + 3x$$

$$x^2 + 3x - 40 = 0$$
$$(x + 8)(x - 5) = 0$$

$$x = -8 \text{ or } x = 5$$

The solution $x = -8$ is not applicable, so the solution $x = 5$ is taken. The width of the rectangle is therefore found to be 5 inches and its width 8 inches.

To Check:

$$(x + 3)x, \text{ where } x = 5$$

A	S	1	2		3	4	5	6
	K	5	+		3	X	5	=
	D	5.	5.		3.	8.	5.	40.

B	S	1	2		3	4	5	6	
	K	5	ENT↑		3	+	5	X	
	D	5.	5.		3	8.	5	40.	

C	S	1	2		3	4	5	6	7
	K	5	+		3	=	X	5	=
	D	5	5.		3	8.	8.	5	40.

6. A square and a rectangle have the same area. The
   length of the rectangle is 3 inches more than the side
   of the square. The width of the rectangle is 2 inches
   less than the side of the square. Find the side of the
   square.

Solution:

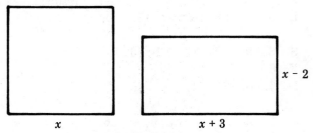

The area of a square is equal to its side squared. If we let
x equal the length of the side of the square, then for the
rectangle

$$\text{length} = x + 3.$$

Furthermore, we are given that the width of the rectangle
is 2 inches less than the side of the square. Therefore,

$$\text{width} = x - 2.$$

We know that the area of a rectangle is given by its length
times its width,

$$\text{area} = \text{length} \times \text{width}$$
$$= (x + 3)(x - 2)$$

Since the areas of the two figures are equal, we have

$$x^2 = (x + 3)(x - 2)$$
$$= x^2 + x - 6$$
$$0 = x - 6$$
$$x = 6$$

Therefore, the side of the square is 6 inches.

To Check:

(a) x^2 and (b) $(x + 3)(x - 2)$, where $x = 6$.

The answers should be identical.

A	S	1	2	3	4	5	6	7	Write down this
	K	6	$\times$	=	6	+	3	=	result.
	D	6.	6.	36.	6.	6.	3.	9.	

	S	8	9	10	11	12	13
	K	6	–	2	$\times$	9	=
	D	6.	6.	2.	4.	9.	36.

B	S	1	2	3	4	5	6
	K	6	F	x^2	6	ENT↑	3
	D	6	6	36.	6	6.	3

	S	7	8	9	10	11	12
	K	+	6	ENT↑	2	–	$\times$
	D	9.	6	6.	2	4.	36.

C	S	1	2	3	4	5	6	7	8
	K	6	x^2	6	+	3	=	STO	1
	D	6	36.	6	6.	3	9.	9.	9.

	S	9	10	11	12	13	14	15	16
	K	6	–	2	=	$\times$	RCL	1	=
	D	6	6.	2	4.	4.	4.	9.	36.

Using the basic calculator, the two expressions for $x = 6$ were found to be equal in 13 steps. The number of steps required using the intermediate calculator was 12. Oddly enough, using the advanced calculator, the number of steps required is seen to be no less than 16. The reason for this is that the memory feature on the SR-51 was utilized instead of manually writing down an intermediate result as was necessary with the basic calculator.

On the SR-51, there are three memory locations into which numbers can be stored. These locations are numbered one, two, and three, respectively. To store a number in the display into one of the memory locations on the SR-51, the key marked STO is pressed, followed by the desired memory location. For example, the key sequence

$$\text{STO} \quad 2$$

will copy the contents of the display into memory location two, leaving the display unaltered.

Similarly, to recall a number which has previously been stored into any of the three memory locations, one simply presses the key marked RCL, followed by the corresponding memory location. Thus, the key sequence

$$\text{RCL} \quad 3$$

will recall the contents of memory location three to the display, leaving the contents of that memory location unaltered.

7. Given that $r = 3.25$, $s = 6.78$, and $y = 201$, calculate the shaded area indicated in the figure below.

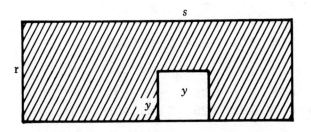

Solution:

The shaded area equals the area of the rectangle minus the area of the square. The area of a rectangle equals the product of its length and its width:

$$\text{area} = \text{length} \times \text{width}$$
$$= s \times r$$
$$= 6.78 \times 3.25$$

The area of a square is equal to the square of one of its sides:

$$\text{area} = (\text{side})^2$$
$$= (y)^2$$
$$= (2.01)^2$$

Thus, we have

$$\text{area of shaded figure} = (6.78)(3.25) - (2.01)^2 .$$

A	S	1	2	3	4		5
	K	6.78	$\times$	3.25	=	Write down	2.01
	D	6.78	6.78	3.25	22.035	this result.	2.01

	S	6	7	8	9	10	11
	K	$\times$	=	-	=	22.035	=
	D	2.01	4.0401	4.0401	0.	22.035	17.9949

B	S	1	2	3	4
	K	6.78	ENT↑	3.25	$\times$
	D	6.78	6.78	3.25	22.035

	S	5	6	7	8
	K	2.01	F	x^2	-
	D	2.01	2.01	4.0401	17.9949

C	S	1	2	3	4	5	6	7
	K	6.78	$\times$	3.25	-	2.01	x^2	=
	D	6.78	6.78	3.25	22.035	2.01	4.0401	17.9949

From each of the above sequences, we see that the area of the shaded figure is 17.9949 square units.

Using the basic calculator, 2.01 is squared using the constant technique and then converted into a constant subtraction factor in order to subtract it from the first intermediate result of 22.035.

7.5 EXERCISES

Now solve the following:

1. Find the area of the shaded portion, when $a = 15.3$ and $b = 2.97$.

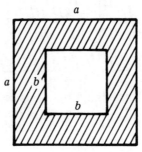

2. Find the area of the figure with the given dimensions.

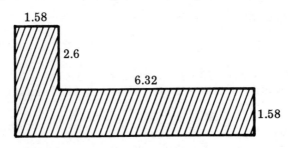

3. Calculate the area of the shaded portion, where (a) $r = 0.58$, $s = 2.68$ and (b) $r = 2.31$, $s = 4.0$.

4. Calculate the area of the shaded portion, where $r = 1.2$, $b = 2.3$, $h = 3.6$, $s = 2.7$, $w = 4.8$, $l = 10.7$.

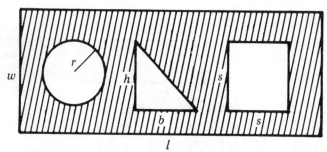

5. The length of a rectangle exceeds its width by 5 inches. If the length of the rectangle is decreased by 3 inches and the width is increased by 4 inches, a new rectangle is formed whose area is 30 square inches more than the area of the original rectangle. Find the dimensions of the original rectangle. Use the calculator to check your solutions.

7.6 SOLVING QUADRATIC EQUATIONS

High school students are asked to solve a great many quadratic equations. Here are some typical examples:

(a) $3x^2 + 2x - 5 = 0$
(b) $10x^2 - 5x + 7 = 0$
(c) $x^2 - 9 = 0$
(d) $x^2 + 3x = 0$
(e) $5x^2 - 2x + 10 = 0$

Notice that each of the above equations has a particular form: first of all, each contains as its highest power of x an x^2 term; secondly, each is set equal to zero. In the event that a quadratic equation is not set equal to zero, we can easily amend it to put it in its so-called standard form. For example, the quadratic equation

$$x^2 - 3x = 2$$

can be set equal to zero by subtracting 2 from both sides of the equation. This transforms the equation into

$$x^2 - 3x - 2 = 0,$$

which is in standard form. The reason why we prefer to present a quadratic in standard form is that once it is in this form, it may be solved very easily, particularly with a pocket calculator.

Each of the quadratic equations cited above—and in fact every quadratic equation—conforms to the following *general* pattern:

$$ax^2 + bx + c = 0,$$

where a is the coefficient of x^2 and is not equal to zero; b is the coefficient of the x term; and c is the constant factor. Therefore, the values of a, b, and c in the equations given above are as follows:

in equation (a), $a = 3$, $b = 2$, $c = -5$
in equation (b), $a = 10$, $b = -5$, $c = 7$
in equation (c), $a = 1$, $b = 0$, $c = -9$
in equation (d), $a = 1$, $b = 3$, $c = 0$
in equation (e), $a = 5$, $b = -2$, $c = 10$

Once values of a, b, and c are known, they may be substituted into a formula which is so important and useful that it is worth memorizing. Here it is:

$$x_1, x_2 = \frac{-b \pm \sqrt{b^2 - 4ac}}{2a}$$

We have written x_1, x_2 because every quadratic equation has two solutions, or roots, each of which satisfies the equation. We could, therefore, have written the equation like this:

$$x_1 = \frac{-b + \sqrt{b^2 - 4ac}}{2a} \qquad x_2 = \frac{-b - \sqrt{b^2 - 4ac}}{2a}$$

In most of our illustrations, the quantity under the square root sign will be positive or zero. This is not to say that if this quantity, called the *discriminant*, is negative, the equation cannot be solved. On the contrary, it certainly can, using the same formula. However, one has to resort to so-called complex arithmetic.

8. Find the roots of the quadratic equation

$$3x^2 + 4x - 20 = 0.$$

Solution:

$$x_1, x_2 = \frac{-b \pm \sqrt{b^2 - 4ac}}{2a}, \text{ where } a = 3, b = 4, c = -20$$

$$= \frac{-4 \pm \sqrt{4^2 - (4)(3)(-20)}}{(2)(3)}$$

Since the basic calculator is seldom equipped with a change-sign key, dealing with negative numbers, as is necessary in solving quadratic equations, becomes somewhat complicated. Moreover, if the basic calculator does not have a square root button, one might have to resort to the Newton-Raphson technique described earlier to find the square root of the discriminant. If the reader does in fact have such a calculator, we leave him to devise his own method. We therefore present solutions to this problem using the intermediate and the advanced calculators.

B	S	1	2	3	4	5	6
	K	4	F	x^2	4	ENT↑	3
	D	4	4	16.	4	4.	3

S	7	8	9	10	11	12
K	×	20	CHS	×	−	√
D	12.	20	−20	−240.	256.	16.

S	13	14	15	16	17	18
K	MS	4	CHS	+	2	ENT↑
D	16	4	−4	12	2	2.

S	19	20	21	22	23	24
K	3	×	÷	4	CHS	MR
D	3	6.	2.	4	−4	16.

S	25	26	27	28	29	30
K	−	2	ENT↑	3	×	÷
D	−20.	2	2.	3	6.	−3.3333333

This sequence using the intermediate calculator with RPN is seen to require 30 steps. Since it uses some unusual techniques, perhaps a short explanation would not be out of order. First, the discriminant is evaluated, and the square root is found and stored in the memory. Since there is both a plus and a minus sign preceding the square root sign, two evaluations must be made. Taking the plus sign first, -4 is added to the contents of the display ($\sqrt{b^2 - 4ac}$) in step 16, and the corresponding first root, namely

$$x_1 = 2,$$

is found in step 21. By a similar method, the second root is found to be

$$x_2 = -3\tfrac{1}{3}.$$

Notice that the square root of the discriminant, which was stored initially in step 13, is used again in step 24, thus saving a little work.

To Check:

In order to be sure that the two roots which we have found are correct, we may substitute each of these values separately into the equation. It follows therefore that $3x^2 + 4x - 20$ should be equal to zero for $x = 2$ and $x = -3\frac{1}{3}$.

B	S	1	2	3	4	5	6	7
	K	3	ENT↑	2	F	x^2	×	4
	D	3	3.	2	2	4	12.	4

	S	8	9	10	11	12	13	14
	K	ENT↑	2	×	+	20	−	3
	D	4.	2	8.	20.	20	0.	3

	S	15	16	17
	K	ENT↑	3.3333333	CHS
	D	3.	3.3333333	−3.3333333

	S	18	19	20
	K	F	x^2	×
	D	−3.3333333	11.11111	33.33333

	S	21	22	23
	K	4	ENT↑	3.3333333
	D	4	4.	3.3333333

	S	24	25	26
	K	CHS	×	+
	D	−3.3333333	−13.333333	19.999997

	S	27	28
	K	20	−
	D	20	−.000003

According to the above sequence, in step 13, the result is

zero, proving that 2 is in fact one of the roots of the equation. In step 28, however, we see that the result is $-.000003$, which is a close approximation to zero. This kind of approximation cannot be avoided since $-3\frac{1}{3}$ is a repeating fraction, and the display of the calculator can only hold a portion of it.

Now, using the advanced calculator:

C	S	1	2	3	4	5	6	7
	K	4	x^2	-	4	×	3	×
	D	4	16.	16.	4	4.	3	12.

	S	8	9	10	11	12	13	14
	K	20	+/-	=	$\sqrt{x}$	STO	1	+
	D	20	-20	256.	16.	16.	16.	16.

	S	15	16	17	18	19	20	21
	K	4	+/-	=	÷	2	÷	3
	D	4	-4	12.	12.	2	6.	3

	S	22	23	24	25	26	27	28
	K	=	4	+/-	-	RCL	1	=
	D	2.	4	-4	-4.	-4.	16.	-20.

	S	29	30	31	32	33
	K	÷	2	÷	3	=
	D	-20.	2	-10.	3	-3.333333333

The only point worth discussing in the above sequence is the sequence of keystrokes in steps 18 through 21 and again in steps 29 through 32. In both cases it was required to divide the contents of the display by 2×3. This was done by first dividing by 2, and then immediately by 3. This takes advantage of the fact that

$$\frac{1}{2 \times 3} = \frac{\frac{1}{2}}{3}.$$

Although it might appear that solving quadratic equations on a pocket calculator is an unduly lengthy and tedious process, once the technique has been mastered, the calculator will prove its worth.

7.7 EXERCISES

Now solve the following quadratic equations.

1. $x^2 + 6x + 5 = 0$
2. $x^2 + 7x = -10$
3. $x^2 + 11x + 8 = -16$
4. $3x^2 + 5x + 2 = 0$
5. $x^2 + 5x + 4 = x$
6. $x^2 = 9$

7.8 PERCENTAGE AND INVESTMENT PROBLEMS

Not only are percentage and investment problems common on examinations, they are often relevant to our personal lives. We might, for example, be confronted with the problem of investing money in one of several different bank accounts, each of which offers a different rate of interest. Armed with a pocket calculator, such decisions may be made on the basis of sound calculations, instead of haphazard guesses or someone else's advice.

9. A set of books was selling at Easter time for $24.00. If this was 80% of the original price, what was the original price?

   Solution:
   Let x = the original price of the set of books. Then 80% of x equals $24.00:

$$.80x = 24.00$$

$$x = \frac{24.00}{.80}$$

A	S	1	2	3	4
	K	24	÷	.80	=
	D	24.	24.	0.80	30.

B	S	1	2	3	4
	K	24	ENT↑	.80	÷
	D	24	24.	.80	30.

C	S	1	2	3	4
	K	24	÷	.80	=
	D	24	24.	0.80	30.

Thus, the original price of the set of books was $30.00. It can easily be checked that 80% of $30.00 equals $24.00.

10. A school bookstore buys 640 felt-tip pens, of which 32 are found to be defective. What percentage of the pens are nondefective?

Solution:

Let x = the percentage of the pens that are nondefective. The number of nondefective pens received by the bookstore equals 640 - 32 = 608. Therefore,

$$x = \frac{608}{640} \times 100$$

That is, the percentage of nondefective pens is found by dividing the number of nondefective pens by the total number of pens and multiplying by 100.

A	S	1	2	3	4	5	6
	K	608	÷	640	×	100	=
	D	608.	608.	640.	0.95	100.	95.

B	S	1	2	3	4	5	6
	K	608	ENT↑	640	÷	100	×
	D	608	608.	640	.95	100	95.

C	S	1	2	3	4	5	6
	K	608	÷	640	×	100	=
	D	608.	608.	640	0.95	100	95.

Thus, we find that 95% of the pens are nondefective.

11. A college student spends $58 a month of his allowance on transportation to school. This turns out to be 20% of his total monthly income. Calculate his monthly income.

Solution:

Let x = the student's monthly income. Then

$$.20x = 58.00$$

$$x = \frac{58.00}{.20}$$

A	S	1	2	3	4
	K	58	÷	.20	=
	D	58.	58.	.20	290.

B	S	1	2	3	4
	K	58	ENT↑	.20	÷
	D	58	58.	.20	290.

C	S	1	2	3	4
	K	58	÷	.20	=
	D	58	58.	.20	290.

From the above sequences, we find that the student's monthly income was $290.

12. A man invests $1500 at 6% interest. How much money will be earned by the end of the year?

Solution:

The standard formula for solving problems of simple interest is

$$i = prt,$$

where i = interest, p = principal amount, r = rate of interest, and t = term, or number of years money is invested. Substituting in the formula, we get

$$i = 1500 \times .06 \times 1$$
$$= 1500 \times .06$$

A	S	1	2	3	4
	K	1500	X	.06	=
	D	1500.	1500.	.06	90.

B	S	1	2	3	4
	K	1500	ENT↑	.06	X
	D	1500	1500.	.06	90.

C	S	1	2	3	4
	K	1500	X	.06	=
	D	1500	1500.	.06	90.

The interest accrued is therefore seen to be $90.

13. Part of a $5000 award is invested at 6% and the remainder at 5%. The interest earned by each of these investments at the end of one year is the same. Find the amount invested at each rate.

Solution:

Let x = the amount of money invested at 6%. Then $5000 - x$ = the amount of money invested at 5%. Since

$$i = prt,$$

the interest earned from the 6% account is

$$i = .06x.$$

By the same token, the interest from the 5% account is

$$i = .05(5000 - x).$$

Now, since the problem states that these two interest amounts are equal, we can equate these two amounts:

$$.06x = .05(5000 - x)$$

A	S	1	2	3	4
	K	.05	X	5000	=
	D	0.05	0.05	5000.	250.

$$.06x = 250 - .05x$$
$$.11x = 250$$
$$x = \frac{250}{.11}$$

A	S	1	2	3	4
	K	250	÷	.11	=
	D	250.	250.	0.11	2272.7272

Thus, the amount invested at 6% is found to be $2272.73.

A	S	1	2	3	4
	K	5000	-	2272.73	=
	D	5000.	5000.	2272.73	2727.27

The amount invested at 5% is therefore $2727.27.

14. A department chairman invested a total of $5,500 in two separate accounts. In the first account, interest was paid at the rate of 7.5%, while the second account

paid interest at the rate of 8%. If the total annual income from the two accounts was \$420, how much was invested in each account?

Solution:

Let x = the amount invested at 8%. Then $5500 - x$ = the amount invested at 7.5%. Since the total income from the two accounts is \$420,

$$.08x + .075(5500 - x) = 420$$

A	S	1	2	3	4
	K	.075	X	5500	=
	D	0.075	0.075	5500	412.5

$$.08x + 412.5 - .075x = 420$$
$$.005x = 7.5$$
$$x = \frac{7.5}{.005}$$

A	S	1	2	3	4
	K	7.5	÷	.005	=
	D	7.5	7.5	0.005	1500.

Thus, we have calculated that the amount invested at 8% was \$1500.

	S	5	6	7	8
	K	5500	-	1500	=
	D	5500.	5500.	1500.	4000.

The amount invested at $7\frac{1}{2}$% is shown to be \$4000.

7.9 MOTION PROBLEMS

15. An automobile having transmission problems was

driven from the owner's house to a gas station at 15 miles per hour. Upon arrival, the gas station was found to be closed. As a result, the car had to be driven back home in reverse at the speed of 5 miles per hour. If the entire trip took 6 hours, how far was the garage?

Solution:

Let x = the amount of time the trip to the garage took, traveling at 15 miles per hour. Then $6 - x$ = the amount of time the trip back took, driving in reverse at the rate of 5 miles per hour.

When dealing with problems of motion, one invariably resorts to the standard formula relating distance traveled to the rate of travel and the amount of travel time:

$$\text{distance} = \text{rate} \times \text{time}$$

The distance from the starting point to the garage is, of course, equal to the distance from the garage to the starting point. This may be expressed as

$$15x = 5(6 - x).$$

Reducing and simplifying, we get

$$15x = 30 - 5x$$
$$20x = 30$$
$$x = \frac{30}{20}$$

A	S	1	2	3	4
	K	30	÷	20	=
	D	30.	30.	20.	1.5

Thus, we find out that it took $1\frac{1}{2}$ hours to reach the garage, traveling at the rate of 15 miles per hour.

To calculate the distance traveled to the garage, we multiply the rate by the time:

```
A  S   1     2     3     4
   K   15    X     1.5   =
   D   15.   15.   1.5   22.5
```

We have therefore shown that the distance to the garage (and also from the garage) was $22\frac{1}{2}$ miles.

16. A girl goes to a summer camp by train, a distance of 156 miles. The trip takes her $2\frac{3}{4}$ hours. Find the average speed for the trip in miles per hour.

   Solution:
   Let x = the average speed for the trip. Since

$$\text{distance} = \text{rate} \times \text{time},$$

we can find the rate by dividing both sides of the formula by time:

$$\text{rate} = \frac{\text{distance}}{\text{time}}$$

$$x = \frac{156}{2.75}$$

```
A  S   1      2      3      4
   K   156    ÷      2.75   =
   D   156.   156.   2.75   56.727272
```

Thus, we find that the average speed of the train was 56.7 miles per hour.

17. Two planes start out at the same time from Kennedy Airport traveling in opposite directions, one north and the other south. The plane traveling north flies 250 miles per hour faster than the one traveling south. After $2\frac{1}{2}$ hours have elapsed, there is a distance of 1250 miles separating them. Find the average speed of the plane traveling south.

Solution:

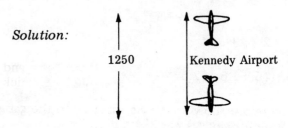

1250   Kennedy Airport

Let x = the speed of the plane traveling south. Then $x + 250$ = the speed of the plane traveling north. To calculate the distance flown by the plane traveling south, we again multiply rate by time:

$$\text{distance} = \text{rate} \times \text{time}$$
$$= x \times 2.5$$
$$= 2.5x$$

Similarly, the distance flown by the plane traveling north is

$$\text{distance} = \text{rate} \times \text{time}$$
$$= (x + 250) \times 2.5$$
$$= 2.5(x + 250)$$
$$= 2.5x + 625$$

The two distances, $2.5x$ and $2.5x + 625$, must total 1250 miles. Therefore,

$$2.5x + 2.5x + 625 = 1250$$
$$5x + 625 = 1250$$
$$5x = 625$$
$$x = \frac{625}{5}$$

A	S	1	2	3	4
	K	625	÷	5	=
	D	625.	625.	5.	125.

From the above, it is clear that the average speed of the plane traveling south was 125 miles per hour.

7.10 COIN PROBLEMS

18. A panhandler, on examining his take at the end of the day, finds that he has collected only nickels, dimes, and quarters. The number of nickels and quarters is the same. However, he has 20 more dimes than quarters. If his total take for the day is $34, how many nickels did he collect?

Solution:

Let x = the number of nickels collected. Then x = the number of quarters collected and $20 + x$ = the number of dimes collected.

Since one nickel is $.05, then x nickels is $.05x$. Similarly, $20 + x$ dimes has a dollar value of $.10(20 + x)$, and x quarters is equivalent to $.25x$.

Since the total value of the coins is stated to be $34.00, we can write the equation

$$.05x + .10(20 + x) + .25x = 34.00$$

In order to clear the decimal fractions, each of the terms on both sides of the equation is multiplied by 100.

$$5x + 10(20 + x) + 25x = 3400$$

Solving for x

$$5x + 200 + 10x + 25x = 3400$$
$$40x + 200 = 3400$$
$$40x = 3200$$
$$x = \frac{3200}{40}$$

A	S	1	2	3	4
	K	3200	$\div$	40	=
	D	3200.	3200.	40.	80.

The panhandler therefore collected 80 nickels. This may be checked directly:

$$.05(80) + .10(20 + 80) + .25(80) = 4.00 + 10.00 + 20.00$$
$$= 34.00$$

7.11 EXERCISES

1. The sum of $3900 is invested in two parts. The first is invested at 6%, while the second is invested at 5% interest. The total annual income generated from these investments amounts to $215. Find the original amounts invested at each rate.

2. A hot corn vendor sold small ears of corn at 15¢ each and large ones for 25¢ each. At the end of the week he found that he had sold 500 ears of corn for a total income of $105. How many small ears of corn were sold?

3. A man decides to invest some money at 5% and twice as much money at 4%. If the yearly income from the two investments is $546, how much money was invested at each of the two rates?

4. A baker sold 25 cookies for $1.66. Some of these cookies cost 6¢ each, while the others cost 10¢ each. Calculate the number of cookies sold at each price.

5. A motorcyclist starts on a trip of 280 miles, stopping once along the way for gas. Before stopping he averaged 50 miles per hour, and for the rest of the trip he averaged 40 miles per hour. If the first part of the trip took two hours longer than the second part, how far had he traveled before he stopped for gas?

8

Geometry

The study of geometry includes congruence, angles, triangles, polygons, circles, area, etc. While it is true that in geometry one learns a lot of facts concerning geometric figures, the main emphasis is on logical thinking and deductive reasoning, which no calculator can help with. However, in those problems in which computation is required, the pocket calculator will permit the student to concentrate more fully on the concepts involved by preventing him from becoming bogged down with mechanical calculations.

8.1 ANGLE SUMS

1. An exterior angle is drawn at the base of an isosceles triangle and is found to be equal to $110°$. Find the number of degrees in the angle at the vertex.

   Solution:
   The solution to this problem rests on three important theorems:

   (1) *The sum of the angles of a triangle equals $180°$.*
   (2) *Supplementary angles are two angles whose sum is a straight angle ($180°$).*
   (3) *The base angles of an isosceles triangle are equal.*

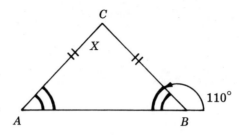

The angle ABC is

$$180° - 110° = 70°$$

Therefore, angle BAC is also $70°$, since the base angles of an isosceles triangle are equal. The angle ACB is therefore equal to

$$180 - 70 - 70.$$

A S	1	2	3	4	5	6
K	180	–	70	–	70	=
D	180.	180.	70.	110.	70.	40.

2. In triangle ABC, the number of degrees in angle ABC is equal to $\frac{1}{4}$ the number of degrees of its complement. Find the number of degrees in angle ABC.

Solution:

Two angles are *complementary* if their sum is equal to $90°$. Therefore,

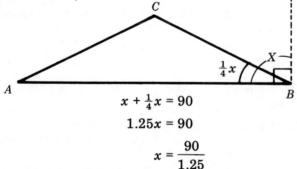

$$x + \tfrac{1}{4}x = 90$$
$$1.25x = 90$$
$$x = \frac{90}{1.25}$$

```
A  S   1     2     3      4
   K   90    ÷     1.25   =
   D   90.   90.   1.25   72.
```

Since angle ABC is equal to $\frac{1}{4}$ of this amount,

$$\text{angle } ABC = \frac{72}{4}$$

```
   S   5     6     7     8
   K   72    ÷     4     =
   D   72.   72.   4.    18.
```

8.2 POLYGONS

3. A regular polygon has 9 sides. Calculate the measure of an interior angle.

Solution:

The number of degrees in each interior angle of a regular polygon of n sides is given in the following formula:

$$\frac{180(n-2)}{n}$$

In this case $n = 9$. Substituting in the formula above, we get

$$\frac{180(9-2)}{9}.$$

```
A  S   1    2     3    4    5      6        7     8
   K   9    -     2    ×    180    ÷        9     =
   D   9.   9.    2.   7.   180.   1260.    9.    140.
```

```
B  S   1      2       3    4       5    6    7       8    9
   K   180    ENT↑    9    ENT↑    2    -    ×       9    ÷
   D   180    180.    9    9.      2    7.   1260.   9    140.
```

4. If each interior angle of a regular polygon contains 144°, what is the number of sides in the polygon?

Solution:

By solving the formula

$$x = \frac{180(n - 2)}{n}$$

for n, we obtain

$$nx = 180(n - 2)$$
$$= 180n - 360$$
$$360 = 180n - nx$$
$$= n(180 - x)$$
$$n = \frac{360}{180 - x},$$

where x is the number of degrees in the measure of an interior angle of the polygon. Therefore,

$$n = \frac{360}{180 - 144}$$

A	S	1	2	3	4	5	6	7	8
	K	180	–	144	=	÷	=	360	=
	D	180.	180.	144.	36.	36.	1.	360.	10.

B	S	1	2	3	4	5	6	7
	K	360	ENT↑	180	ENT↑	144	–	÷
	D	360	360.	180	180.	144	36.	10.

C	S	1	2	3	4	5	6	7	8
	K	180	–	144	=	÷	360	$x \leftrightharpoons y$	=
	D	180.	180.	144.	36.	36.	360	36.	10.

Thus, we find that the polygon has ten sides.

By way of a reminder, we would mention that using the basic calculator, advantage was taken of the constant feature in calculating the result. In steps 5 through 8, the denominator was turned into a constant divisor so that the numerator could be entered and the proper division performed, a technique which we illustrated earlier in the book.

On the advanced calculator, the computation was done in reverse, as if what we wanted to calculate was

$$\frac{180 - 144}{360},$$

but the correct answer was achieved by using the x to y interchange key.

8.3 THE PYTHAGOREAN THEOREM

One of the most frequently recurring theorems of geometry is the one associating the lengths of the three sides of a right triangle that is named in honor of its discoverer, the sixth-century B.C. Greek philosopher Pythagoras. His theorem, known as the Pythagorean Theorem, states that *the sum of the squares of the lengths of the sides of a right triangle is equal to the square of the length of the hypotenuse.* Although this statement of the theorem may sound complicated, it is really quite simple, and its applications are limitless. To understand the implications of this theorem, let us examine a right triangle.

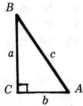

Triangle ABC has a right angle ($90°$) at C. According to the Pythagorean Theorem,

$$a^2 + b^2 = c^2.$$

Thus, given the values of any two sides, the third side can always be calculated by applying one of the following three versions of the Pythagorean Theorem.

$$a = \sqrt{c^2 - b^2}$$
$$b = \sqrt{c^2 - a^2}$$
$$c = \sqrt{a^2 + b^2}$$

5. Find the diagonal of a rectangle whose sides are 12 and 16.

   Solution:

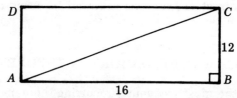

In the above diagram, the diagonal *AC* of rectangle *ABCD* forms a right triangle with the sides *AB* and *BC*. The length of *AC* can therefore be calculated by the Pythagorean Theorem:

$$AC = \sqrt{(12)^2 + (16)^2}$$

Since a square root is required, no solution is offered using the basic calculator.

B	S	1	2	3	4	5	6	7	8
	K	12	F	x^2	16	F	x^2	+	$\sqrt{}$
	D	12	12	144.	16	16	256.	400.	20.

C	S	1	2	3	4	5	6	7
	K	12	x^2	+	16	x^2	=	$\sqrt{x}$
	D	12	144	144.	16	256.	400.	20.

6. An equilateral triangle has a side equal to 10 inches. Find the length of the altitude, to two decimal places.

Solution:

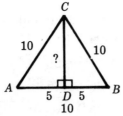

The triangle is equilateral, therefore *each* side is equal to 10 inches. Since the altitude of an equilateral triangle bisects the base, $AD = DB = 5$. Since CD is an altitude in triangle ABC, triangles ADC and BDC are right triangles. We can therefore apply the Pythagorean Theorem to compute the length of the altitude CD:

$$CD = \sqrt{(10)^2 - (5)^2}$$

B	S	1	2	3	4	5	6	7	8
	K	10	F	x^2	5	F	x^2	–	$\sqrt{}$
	D	10	10	100.	5	5	25.	75.	8.660254

C	S	1	2	3	4	5	6	7
	K	10	x^2	–	5	x^2	=	$\sqrt{x}$
	D	10	100.	100.	5	25.	75.	8.660254038

The length of the altitude in an equilateral triangle whose side is 10 inches is therefore equal to 8.66 inches, to two decimal places.

7. Triangle ABC has a right angle at C. From C an altitude is constructed to the hypotenuse AB, meeting it at D. If $AC = 25$ and $CD = 24$, calculate AD.

Solution:

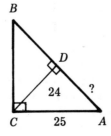

Triangle ACD is a right triangle and therefore the Pythagorean Theorem may be applied:

$$24^2 + AD^2 = 25^2$$
$$AD^2 = 25^2 - 24^2$$
$$AD = \sqrt{25^2 - 24^2}$$

B	S	1	2	3	4	5	6	7	8
	K	25	F	x^2	24	F	x^2	–	$\sqrt{}$
	D	25	25	625.	24	24	576.	49.	7.

C	S	1	2	3	4	5	6	7
	K	25	x^2	–	24	x^2	=	$\sqrt{x}$
	D	25	625.	625.	24	576.	49.	7.

8.4 THE DISTANCE FORMULA

An extension of the Pythagorean Theorem is used when calculating the distance between two points located on a plane. In the diagram below, A and B are arbitrarily selected points with the coordinates (x_1, y_1) and (x_2, y_2), respectively.

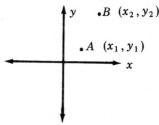

The distance between A and B is the length of a straight line drawn between them. This line may be regarded as the hypotenuse of a triangle whose two sides are parallel to the x and y axes as shown below.

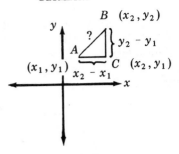

The length AB may therefore be defined according to the following formula:

$$\overline{AB}^2 = \overline{AC}^2 + \overline{BC}^2$$
$$= (x_2 - x_1)^2 + (y_2 - y_1)^2$$
$$\overline{AB} = \sqrt{(x_2 - x_1)^2 + (y_2 - y_1)^2}$$

The last version of the formula, which is the one we shall use in solving the two problems which follow, is known as the *distance formula*.

8. Find the distance between points (2, 4) and (5, 2).

Solution:
The first point is (2, 4). The second point is (5, 2). According to the formula, the distance d between the two points is

$$d = \sqrt{(x_1 - x_2)^2 + (y_1 - y_2)^2}$$
$$= \sqrt{(2 - 5)^2 + (4 - 2)^2}$$
$$= \sqrt{(-3)^2 + (2)^2}$$

B	S	1	2	3	4	5	6	7	8	9
	K	3	CHS	F	x^2	2	F	x^2	+	$\sqrt{}$
	D	3	-3	-3	9.	2	2	4.	13.	3.6055512

C	S	1	2	3	4	5	6	7	8
	K	3	+/-	x^2	+	2	x^2	=	$\sqrt{x}$
	D	3	-3	9.	9.	2	4.	13.	3.605551275

9. A circle whose center is at C $(-3, 5)$ passes through point D $(-2, 7)$. Find the length of the radius CD, to two decimal places.

Solution:

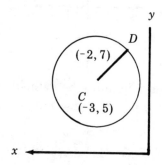

Let the coordinates of point C be (x_1, y_1). Then

$$x_1 = -3, \quad y_1 = 5$$

Let the coordinates of point D be (x_2, y_2). Then

$$x_2 = -2, \quad y_2 = 7$$

By the distance formula,

$$\overline{CD} = \sqrt{(x_1 - x_2)^2 + (y_1 - y_2)^2}$$
$$= \sqrt{(-3 - (-2))^2 + (5 - 7)^2}$$
$$= \sqrt{(-1)^2 + (-2)^2}$$

B	S	1	2		3	4	5	6		7	8	9	10
	K	1	CHS		F	x^2	2	CHS		F	x^2	+	$\sqrt{\ }$
	D	1	-1		-1	1.	2	-2		-2	4.	5	2.2360679

C	S	1	2	3	4	5	6	7	8	9
	K	1	+/-	x^2	+	2	+/-	x^2	=	$\sqrt{x}$
	D	1	-1	1.	1.	2	-2	4.	5.	2.236067977

Thus, we find that the radius of the circle C is equal to 2.24, to two decimal places.

8.5 FINDING THE AREA OF A TRIANGLE

To calculate the area of a triangle, multiply one-half of the base by the perpendicular height (the altitude) of the triangle.

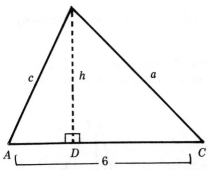

In triangle ABC shown above, BD is perpendicular to base AC. Thus, we can calculate the area of the triangle by multiplying one-half of the base (b) by the perpendicular height (h) of triangle ABC:

$$\text{area} = \tfrac{1}{2} \,(\text{base} \times \text{height})$$
$$\text{area} = \tfrac{1}{2}\, bh$$

10. In triangle ABC, $b = 12.2$ inches and the altitude BD to side AC is 5.2 inches. Find the area of the triangle.

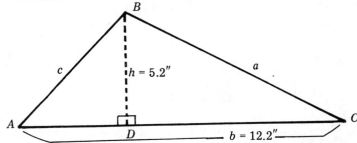

Solution:

$$\text{area} = \tfrac{1}{2} bh$$
$$= \tfrac{1}{2} (12.2)(5.2)$$

A	S	1	2	3	4	5	6
	K	.5	×	12.2	×	5.2	=
	D	0.5	0.5	12.2	6.1	5.2	31.72

The area of triangle *ABC* is thus shown to be 31.72 square inches.

11. The area of a triangle is 20.25. If a side of the triangle is 4, find the altitude drawn to that side.

Solution:

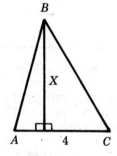

$$\text{area} = \tfrac{1}{2} bh$$
$$20.25 = \tfrac{1}{2} (4)x$$
$$20.25 = 2x$$
$$x = \frac{20.25}{2}$$

A	S	1	2	3	4
	K	20.25	÷	2	=
	D	20.25	20.25	2.	10.125

The length of the altitude is therefore found to be 10.125.

8.6 FINDING THE AREA OF AN EQUILATERAL TRIANGLE

The area of an equilateral triangle, the length of whose side is represented by s, is given by the formula

$$\text{area} = \frac{s^2}{4}\sqrt{3}.$$

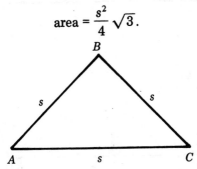

12. Find the area, to the nearest tenth, of an equilateral triangle whose side is 9.

Solution:

$$\text{area} = \frac{9^2}{4}\sqrt{3}$$

B	S	1	2	3	4	5	6	7	8
	K	9	F	x^2	4	÷	3	√	X
	D	9	9	81.	4	20.25	3	1.7320508	35.074028

C	S	1	2	3	4	5	6
	K	9	x^2	÷	4	X	3
	D	9	81.	81.	4	20.25	3

S	7	8
K	$\sqrt{x}$	=
D	1.732050808	35.07402885

It is clear from the above that the area of the triangle is 35.1 square units, to the nearest tenth.

8.7   FINDING THE AREA OF A PARALLELOGRAM

The area of a parallelogram is equal to the product of one side and the perpendicular drawn to that side:

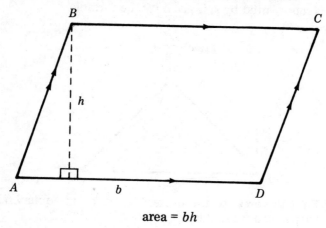

area = bh

13.   Find the area of parallelogram $ABCD$ shown below.

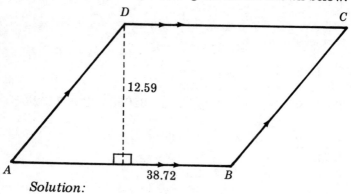

Solution:

area = (38.72) (12.59)

A	S	1	2	3	4
	K	12.59	×	38.72	=
	D	12.59	12.59	38.72	487.4848

8.8 FINDING THE AREA OF A TRAPEZOID

The area of a trapezoid is equal to one-half the product of its altitude and the sum of its bases:

$$\text{area} = \tfrac{1}{2}(b_1 + b_2)h$$

14. Find the area of the trapezoid $ABCD$ if $AB = 10.3$ inches, $CD = 6.6$ inches, and altitude $DE = 7.43$ inches.

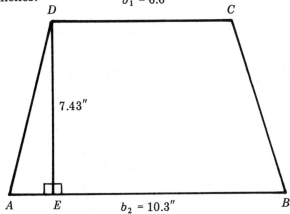

Solution:

$$\text{area} = \tfrac{1}{2}(b_1 + b_2)h$$
$$\text{area} = \tfrac{1}{2}(10.3 + 6.6)(7.43)$$

A	S	1	2	3	4	5	6	7	8
	K	10.3	+	6.6	×	.5	×	7.43	=
	D	10.3	10.3	6.6	16.9	0.5	8.45	7.43	62.7835

8.9 FINDING THE CIRCUMFERENCE OF A CIRCLE

The circumference of a circle is found by multiplying twice π (≈ 3.14159) by the radius of the circle:

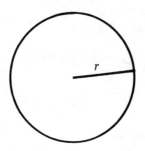

$$\text{circumference} = 2 \times \pi \times \text{radius}$$
$$C = 2\pi r$$

15. Find the circumference of circle O, whose radius is 2.372.

A   S   1   2   3   4   5   6
     K   2   ×   3.14159   ×   2.372   =
     D   2.   2.   3.14159   6.28318   2.372   14.903702

B   S   1   2   3
     K   2   ENT↑ π
     D   2   2.   3.1415926

     S   4   5   6
     K   ×   2.372   ×
     D   6.2831852   2.372   14.903715

C	S	1	2	3
	K	2	×	π
	D	2	2.	3.141592654

	S	4	5	6
	K	×	2.372	=
	D	6.283185307	2.372	14.90371555

8.10 FINDING THE AREA OF A CIRCLE

The area of a circle is equal to the product of π (≈ 3.14159) and the square of its radius:

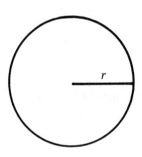

$$\text{area} = \pi \times (\text{radius})^2$$
$$\text{area} = \pi r^2$$

16. Find the area of a circle whose radius is .985 inches.

A	S	1	2	3
	K	.985	×	=
	D	0.985	0.985	0.970225

	S	4	5	6
	K	×	3.14159	=
	D	0.970225	3.14159	3.0480491

B	S	1	2	3
	K	π	ENT↑	.985
	D	3.1415926	3.1415926	.985

	S	4	5	6
	K	F	x^2	X
	D	.985	.970225	3.0480516

C	S	1	2	3
	K	π	X	.985
	D	3.141592654	3.141592654	0.985

	S	4	5
	K	x^2	=
	D	0.970225	3.048051732

There is a slight discrepancy using the three calculators, but the answer is clearly 3.048 square inches, to the third decimal place.

17. Find the area of a circle whose diameter is 2.379 inches.

Solution:

The problem asks for us to compute the area given the *diameter* of the circle. Since we know that the diameter equals twice the radius,

$$d = 2r, \text{ or } r = \frac{d}{2}.$$

We can derive the formula for the area of a circle, given its diameter:

$$\text{area} = \pi r^2$$
$$= \pi \left(\frac{d}{2}\right)^2$$

$$= \frac{\pi d^2}{4}$$

We are told that $d = 2.379$. Therefore,

$$\text{area} = \frac{\pi (2.379)^2}{4}.$$

A   S   1   2   3   4

S	1	2	3	4
K	2.379	X	=	X
D	2.379	2.379	5.659641	5.659641

S	5	6	7	8
K	3.14159	÷	4	=
D	3.14159	17.780271	4.	4.4450677

B

S	1	2	3	4
K	π	ENT↑	2.379	F
D	3.1415926	3.1415926	2.379	2.379

S	5	6	7	8
K	x^2	X	4	÷
D	5.659641	17.780286	4	4.4450715

C

S	1	2	3	4
K	π	X	2.379	x^2
D	3.141592654	3.141592654	2.379	5.659641

S	5	6	7
K	÷	4	=
D	17.78028659	4	4.445071647

18. Find the area of a circle whose circumference is 29.78.

Solution:

$$C = 2\pi r$$

Solving for r, the radius of the circle, we get

$$r = \frac{C}{2\pi}$$

$$= \frac{29.78}{2\pi}.$$

A	S	1	2	3	4	5	6
	K	29.78	÷	2	÷	3.14159	=
	D	29.78	29.78	2.	14.89	3.14159	4.7396382

B	S	1	2	3	4	5	6
	K	29.78	ENT↑	2	÷	π	÷
	D	29.78	29.78	2	14.89	3.1415926	4.7396342

C	S	1	2	3	4	5
	K	29.78	÷	2	÷	π
	D	29.78	29.78	2	14.89	3.141592654

	S	6
	K	=
	D	4.739634205

If we insert the value of r just calculated into our formula for computing the area of a circle (area $= \pi r^2$), we get

$$\text{area} = \pi(4.7396)^2.$$

A	S	1	2	3	4
	K	4.7396	X	=	X
	D	4.7396	4.7396	22.463808	22.463808

	S	5	6
	K	3.14159	=
	D	3.14159	70.572074

B	S	1	2	3	4
	K	π	ENT↑	4.7396	F
	D	3.1415926	3.1415926	4.7396	4.7396

	S	5	6
	K	x^2	X
	D	22.463808	70.572132

C	S	1	2	3
	K	π	X	4.7396
	D	3.141592654	3.141592654	4.7396

	S	4	5
	K	x^2	=
	D	22.46380816	70.57213469

Thus, we find that the area of the circle is 70.57.

8.11 THE TRIGONOMETRY OF THE RIGHT TRIANGLE

A natural extension of the study of the Pythagorean Theorem is an exploration of the relationships between the angles and the lengths of the sides of right triangles, including the fundamental concepts of sine, cosine, and tangent and their relationships to each other.

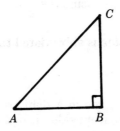

Triangle *ABC* has a right angle at *B*. Concentrating for the moment on angle *C*, we can describe the side *AB* as that side of triangle *ABC* that is *opposite* angle *C*. Similarly, we can refer to the side *BC* as the side *adjacent* to angle *C*. The hypotenuse, *AC*, is always referred to as the *hypotenuse*.

By the same token, the side opposite angle *A* is the side *BC*, while the side adjacent to angle *A* is side *AB*.

The three words *opposite*, *adjacent*, and *hypotenuse* are the keys to the understanding of the trigonometric functions.

Sine

The *sine* of an angle in a right triangle is the value of the length of the opposite side divided by the length of the hypotenuse:

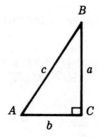

$$\text{sine } A = \frac{a}{c}$$

$$\text{sine } B = \frac{b}{c}$$

Usually, the word *sine* is abbreviated to *sin*.

Cosine

The *cosine* of an angle in a right triangle is the value of the length of the adjacent side divided by the length of the hypotenuse:

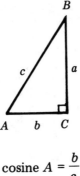

$$\text{cosine } A = \frac{b}{c}$$

$$\text{cosine } B = \frac{a}{c}$$

Usually, the word *cosine* is abbreviated to *cos*.

Tangent

The *tangent* of an angle in a right triangle is found by dividing the length of the side opposite the angle by the length of its adjacent side:

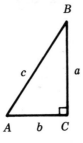

$$\text{tangent } A = \frac{a}{b}$$

$$\text{tangent } B = \frac{b}{a}$$

Usually, the word *tangent* is abbreviated to *tan*.

These three ratios may be remembered quite easily by means of the following mnemonic:

soh cah toa,

which is a shorthand way of remembering that the sine (s) is the "opposite (o) over the hypotenuse (h)," the cosine (c) is the "adjacent (a) over the hypotenuse (h)," and the tangent (t) is the "opposite (o) over the adjacent (a)."

19. In the right triangle below, calculate sin A, cos A, tan A, sin B, cos B, tan B.

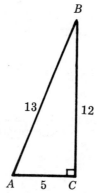

Solution:

$$\sin A = \frac{\text{opposite}}{\text{hypotenuse}} = \frac{12}{13}$$

A S   1   2   3   4
     K 12 ÷   13   =
     D 12. 12. 13. 0.9230769

$$\cos A = \frac{\text{adjacent}}{\text{hypotenuse}} = \frac{5}{13}$$

A   S   1   2   3   4
    K   5   ÷   13   =
    D   5.   5.   13.   0.3846153

$$\tan A = \frac{\text{opposite}}{\text{adjacent}} = \frac{12}{5}$$

A   S   1   2   3   4
    K   12   ÷   5   =
    D   12.   12.   5.   2.4

$$\sin B = \frac{\text{opposite}}{\text{hypotenuse}} = \frac{5}{13}$$

A   S   1   2   3   4
    K   5   ÷   13   =
    D   5.   5.   13.   0.3846153

$$\cos B = \frac{\text{adjacent}}{\text{hypotenuse}} = \frac{12}{13}$$

A   S   1   2   3   4
    K   12   ÷   13   =
    D   12.   12.   13.   0.9230769

$$\tan B = \frac{\text{opposite}}{\text{adjacent}} = \frac{5}{12}$$

A   S   1   2   3   4
    K   5   ÷   12   =
    D   5.   5.   12.   0.4166666

20. A vertical flagpole in a military academy casts a shadow 30 feet long at the time of day when the angle of elevation of the sun is 35°. Calculate the height of the pole to the nearest foot.

Solution:

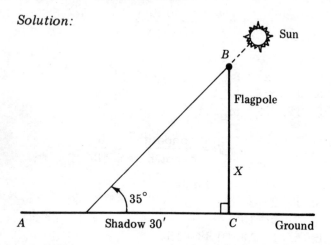

In the above diagram, the flagpole forms a right angle with the ground. We wish to calculate the height of the flagpole, which is the side opposite the 35° angle. We are given that the side adjacent the 35° angle is 30 feet, which is the length of the shadow cast by the flagpole. This should bring to mind the tangent formula:

$$\tan A = \frac{\text{opposite}}{\text{adjacent}}$$

$$\tan 35° = \frac{x}{30}$$

Solving for x, we obtain

$$x = 30 \times \tan 35°.$$

B	S	1	2	3	4	5
	K	30	ENT↑	35	tan	×
	D	30	30.	35	.7002075	21.006225

C	S	Switch slide R-D	1	2	3
	K	to D for degrees.	30	X	35
	D		30	30.	35

S	4	5
K	tan	=
D	.7002075382	21.00622615

The flagpole is therefore calculated to be 21 feet, to the nearest foot. It is pointed out in passing that in calculating an expression such as $30 \times \tan 35°$, one has to be sure that the calculator which one is using permits the computation of the expression in the order stated. A little experimentation with a particular calculator will soon establish the method to be used.

8.12 EXERCISES

1. The length of a side of an equilateral triangle is 7.6. Calculate the area of the equilateral triangle.

2. Calculate the length of a line segment connecting two points whose coordinates are $(3, -1)$ and $(6, 5)$.

3. Calculate the area of a circle whose circumference is 64.87.

4. Calculate the number of degrees in an interior angle of a regular octagon.

5. The length of each leg of an isosceles triangle is 13.4 and the length of the base is 10.9. Calculate the length of the altitude drawn to the base.

6. The area of a trapezoid whose bases measure 6.31 and 14.23 is 80.65. Calculate the length of the altitude of the trapezoid.

7. Calculate the number of degrees in the measure of each exterior angle of a regular polygon of 10 sides. (*Hint:* In any polygon, an interior angle is supplementary to its adjacent exterior angle.)

8. The hypotenuse of a right triangle measures 15.97. If the length of one leg is twice the length of the

other leg, what is the length of the smaller leg?

9. Calculate the area of a triangle whose base measures 15.68 and whose height is 4.9872.

10. In right triangle ABC shown below, calculate (a) sin A, (b) cos B, and (c) tan A.

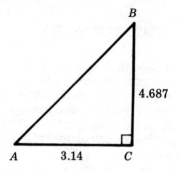

11. If the diameter of a circle measures 2.96, calculate its area and its circumference.

9
Trigonometry

With the material covered in this chapter—trigonometry, logarithms, progressions—the pocket calculator ceases to be an item of prestige and becomes a tool worth its weight in gold. Because of the sophistication required by these advanced subjects, the basic calculator will, for the most part, not be used.

In most examinations, students are provided with suitable logarithmic and trigonometric tables and, for the present at least, chances are that he will *not* be permitted the use of a pocket calculator during the examination. It is for this reason, that we strongly urge you to familiarize yourself with the tables first so that you become expert in their use. The calculator can then be used to maximum advantage in *checking* the solutions. In this manner, the calculator does not become a substitute for the techniques that must be learned, but rather a unique device for reinforcement and verification.

9.1 VERIFYING TRIGONOMETRIC IDENTITIES

It is standard practice to teach methods of proving some of the better known trigonometric identities. This not only provides the student with a sense of satisfaction when he proves an identity but also helps to discipline his mind in much the same way as the proofs in geometry. The calculator cannot in any way assist the student in proving trigonometric identities, but we shall show how it can be used to verify them.

Verify the trigonometric identity $\sin^2 x + \cos^2 x = 1$.

Solution:

If the above identity holds, it has to be true for every angle x for which the function is defined. Verify the identity for

$$x = -5°, 10°, 130°.$$

B	S	1	2	3	4
	K	5	CHS	sin	F
	D	5	-5	-.0871557	-.0871557

	S	5	6	7	8
	K	x^2	5	CHS	cos
	D	.00759611	5	-5	.9961947

	S	9	10	11	12
	K	F	x^2	+	10
	D	.9961947	.99240388	.99999999	10

	S	13	14	15	16
	K	sin	F	x^2	10
	D	.1736482	.1736482	.03015369	10

	S	17	18	19	20
	K	cos	F	x^2	+
	D	.9848078	.9848078	.9698464	1.

	S	21	22	23	24
	K	130	sin	F	x^2
	D	130	.7660445	.7660445	.58682417

S	25	26	27	28
K	130	cos	F	x^2
D	130	−.6427876	−.6427876	.41317589

S	29
K	+
D	1.

C

S	1	2	3
K	5	+/−	sin
D	5	−5	−.0071557427

S	4	5	6
K	x^2	+	5
D	.0075961235	.0075961235	5

S	7	8	9
K	+/−	cos	x^2
D	−5	.9961946981	.9924038765

S	10	11	12
K	=	10	sin
D	1.	10	.1736481777

S	13	14	15
K	x^2	+	10
D	.0301536896	.0301536896	10

S	16	17	18
K	cos	x^2	=
D	0.984807753	.9698463104	1.

S	19	20	21
K	130	sin	x^2
D	130	.7660444431	.5868240888

S	22	23	24
K	+	130	cos
D	.5868240888	130	⁻.6427876097

S	25	26
K	x^2	=
D	.4131759112	1.

In the reverse Polish notation shown in B above, we find that when using the value $-5°$ for the value of x, $\sin^2 x + \cos^2 x = .999999999$, rather than exactly 1. This is not a function of reverse Polish notation, but rather reflects the limitations of the calculator. For when $x = 10°$ (step 12) and when $x = 130°$ (step 21), we find that the identity does in fact equal exactly 1. On the advanced calculator, the identity checks out to 1 in each case.

It cannot be overemphasized that the above sequences do not constitute a "proof" of the trigonometric identity; they merely *confirm* empirically that it holds for the three cases tested.

Verify that the identity $\sin 2\theta = 2 \sin \theta \cos \theta$ is valid for the angle $\theta = 20°$.

Solution:

B	S	1	2	3	4
	K	20	ENT↑	2	×
	D	20	20.	2	40.

S	5	6	7	8
K	sin	MS	2	ENT↑
D	.6427876	.6427876	2	2.

S	9	10	11	12
K	20	sin	×	20
D	20	.3420202	.6840404	20

S	13	14	15	16
K	cos	X	MR	–
D	.9396927	.64278777	.6427876	.00000017

C	S	1	2	3	4
	K	20	X	2	=
	D	20	20.	2	40.

S	5	6	7	8
K	sin	–	2	X
D	.6427876097	.6427876097	2	2.

S	9	10	11	12
K	20	sin	X	20
D	20	.3420201433	.6840402866	20

S	13	14
K	cos	=
D	.9396926208	6.–13

From the above we find that using $20°$ as the value for θ, the identity $\sin 2\theta = 2 \sin \theta \cos \theta$ holds. Using the intermediate calculator, the difference between the left and right hand sides of the above identity comes to .00000017, while on the advanced calculator the difference is even smaller; expressed in scientific notation, the difference was found to be 6.0×10^{-13}. Both results are very close approximations to zero and are not exactly equal to zero only because of the limitation of the calculators.

9.2 THE LAW OF SINES

An interesting and useful law which relates the sides of any triangle to the sines of their opposite angles is the Law of Sines, which is generally stated in the following way:

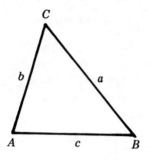

$$\frac{a}{\sin A} = \frac{b}{\sin B} = \frac{c}{\sin C}$$

In triangle ABC, $\sin A = .123$, $\sin B = .543$, and $b = 15$. Find a, to the nearest tenth.

Solution:

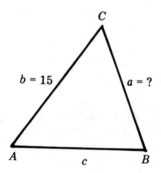

In this problem, we are told the values of $\sin A$, $\sin B$, and b. The unknown in this case is a. We can therefore solve the problem by confining our attention to a shortened version of the Law of Sines as stated above, namely,

$$\frac{a}{\sin A} = \frac{b}{\sin B},$$

where $\sin A = .123$, $\sin B = .543$, and $b = 15$. Therefore,

$$\frac{a}{.123} = \frac{15}{.543}.$$

Solving for a, we obtain

$$a = \frac{(15)\,(.123)}{.543}.$$

A	S	1	2	3	4	5	6
	K	15	X	.123	÷	.543	=
	D	15.	15.	0.123	1.845	0.543	3.39779

Thus, we find that a equals 3.4, to the nearest tenth.

In triangle DEF, $f = 36.5$, $d = 18$, $\sin D = .4$. Find the value of angle F, to the nearest tenth.

Solution:

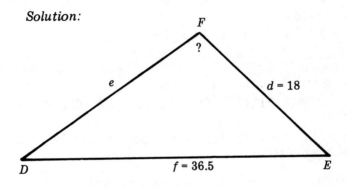

$$\frac{d}{\sin D} = \frac{f}{\sin F}$$

solving for $\sin F$,

$$\sin F = \frac{f \times \sin D}{d}.$$

Thus,

$$F = \sin^{-1}\left(\frac{f \times \sin D}{d}\right),$$

where $f = 36.5$, $d = 18$, and $\sin D = .4$. Therefore,

$$F = \sin^{-1}\left(\frac{36.5 \times .4}{18}\right)$$

B	S	1	2	3	4	5
	K	36.5	ENT↑	.4	×	18
	D	36.5	36.5	.4	14.6	18

	S	6	7	8
	K	÷	F	$\sin^{-1}$
	D	.81111111	.81111111	54.20463

C	S	1	2	3	4	5
	K	36.5	×	.4	÷	18
	D	36.5	36.5	.4	14.6	18

	S	6	7	8
	K	=	INV	sin
	D	.8111111111	.8111111111	54.20463246

It is clear from the above that angle F measures $54.2°$, to the nearest tenth.

9.3 THE LAW OF COSINES

Another interesting and useful trigonometric relationship is demonstrated by the Law of Cosines, which states that in any triangle, the square of any side of the triangle is equal to the sum of the squares of the other two sides, minus twice the product of these other two sides and the cosine of their included angle. This law may be expressed as

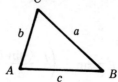

$$a^2 = b^2 + c^2 - 2bc \, (\cos A),$$
$$b^2 = c^2 + a^2 - 2ca \, (\cos B),$$
$$c^2 = a^2 + b^2 - 2ab \, (\cos C).$$

Solving these equations for cos A, cos B, and cos C, we get

$$\cos A = \frac{b^2 + c^2 - a^2}{2bc},$$

$$\cos B = \frac{c^2 + a^2 - b^2}{2ca},$$

$$\cos C = \frac{a^2 + b^2 - c^2}{2ab}.$$

Even though these formulas might look intimidating, with a little effort they can be either remembered or derived.

In triangle ABC shown below, $b = 5.1$, $c = 4$, cos $A = .1$. Find the value of a, to the nearest hundredth.

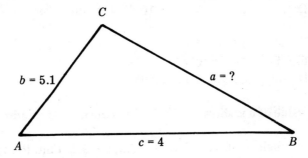

Solution:

$$a^2 = b^2 + c^2 - 2bc \, (\cos A)$$

Therefore,

$$a = \sqrt{b^2 + c^2 - 2bc \, (\cos A)}$$
$$a = \sqrt{(5.1)^2 + (4)^2 - 2(5.1)(4)(.1)}$$

B	S	1	2	3	4	5	6
	K	5.1	F	x^2	4	F	x^2
	D	5.1	5.1	26.01	4	4	16

S	7	8	9	10	11	12
K	+	2	ENT↑	5.1	×	4
D	42.01	2	2.	5.1	10.2	4

S	13	14	15	16	17
K	×	.1	×	−	√
D	40.8	.1	4.08	37.93	6.1587336

C	S	1	2	3	4	5	6
	K	5.1	x^2	+	4	x^2	−
	D	5.1	26.01	26.01	4	16.	42.01

S	7	8	9	10	11	12
K	2	×	5.1	×	4	×
D	2	2.	5.1	10.2	4	40.8

S	13	14	15
K	.1	=	$\sqrt{x}$
D	4.08	37.93	6.158733636

The value of a is shown to be 6.16, to the nearest hundredth.

In triangle ABC, $a = 5.6$, $b = 7.2$, $c = 6.4$. Find the value of angle B, to the nearest tenth.

Solution:

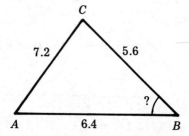

According to the Law of Cosines, we have an expression for computing the value of cos B in terms of a, b, and c. Namely,

$$\cos B = \frac{c^2 + a^2 - b^2}{2ca}.$$

Therefore,

$$B = \cos^{-1}\left(\frac{c^2 + a^2 - b^2}{2ca}\right)$$

$$B = \cos^{-1}\left(\frac{(6.4)^2 + (5.6)^2 - (7.2)^2}{2(6.4)(5.6)}\right).$$

B	S	1	2	3	4	5	6
	K	6.4	F	x^2	5.6	F	x^2
	D	6.4	6.4	40.96	5.6	5.6	31.36

	S	7	8	9	10	11	12
	K	+	7.2	F	x^2	–	2
	D	72.32	7.2	7.2	51.84	20.48	2

	S	13	14	15	16	17
	K	÷	6.4	÷	5.6	÷
	D	10.24	6.4	1.6	5.6	.28571428

C	S	1	2	3	4	5	6
	K	6.4	x^2	+	5.6	x^2	–
	D	6.4	40.96	40.96	5.6	31.36	72.32

	S	7	8	9	10	11	12
	K	7.2	x^2	=	÷	2	÷
	D	7.2	51.84	20.48	20.48	2	10.24

	S	13	14	15	16
	K	6.4	÷	5.6	=
	D	6.4	1.6	5.6	.2857142857

Thus, we find that angle B is .3°, calculated to the nearest tenth. In both cases, the fraction was calculated by successive divisions of the numerator by each of the terms of the denominator. Perhaps it should be mentioned that when solving the problem using the advanced calculator, it was necessary to press the equal button in step 9 to complete the calculation of the numerator.

9.4 THE AREA OF A TRIANGLE

The area of a triangle is equal to one-half the product of any two sides of the triangle and the sine of the included angle. In triangle ABC, the area may be calculated by using any of the following formulas:

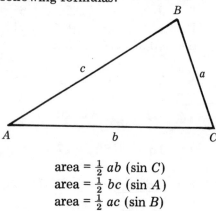

$$\text{area} = \tfrac{1}{2}\, ab\, (\sin C)$$
$$\text{area} = \tfrac{1}{2}\, bc\, (\sin A)$$
$$\text{area} = \tfrac{1}{2}\, ac\, (\sin B)$$

Find the area of a triangle if two sides of the triangle are 3.48 and 2.76 and the included angle measures 33°.

Solution:

$$\text{area} = \tfrac{1}{2}\, ab\, (\sin C)$$
$$= \tfrac{1}{2}\, (3.48)\, (2.76)\, \sin 33°$$

B	S	1	2	3	4	5	6
	K	.5	ENT↑	3.48	X	2.76	X
	D	.5	.5	3.48	1.74	2.76	4.8024

S	7	8	9
K	33	sin	×
D	33	.544639	2.6155743

C	S	1	2	3	4	5	6	7
	K	.5	×	3.48	×	2.76	×	33
	D	0.5	0.5	3.48	1.74	2.76	4.8024	33

S	8	9
K	sin	=
D	0.544639035	2.615574502

Thus, we see that the area of the triangle is equal to 2.62 square units, rounded to two decimal places.

Find the measure of the included angle of a triangle whose area is 30.65 square inches and whose sides measure 10.29 inches and 13.85 inches.

Solution:

In this case, we wish to know the measure of angle C. Solving for C in the formula, we get

$$\text{area} = \tfrac{1}{2}\, ab\, (\sin C)$$

$$\sin C = \frac{\text{area}}{\tfrac{1}{2}\, ab}$$

$$C = \sin^{-1}\left(\frac{2 \times \text{area}}{ab}\right)$$

$$= \sin^{-1}\left(\frac{(2)\,(30.65)}{(10.29)\,(13.85)}\right).$$

B	S	1	2	3	4
	K	2	ENT↑	30.65	×
	D	2	2.	30.65	61.3

S	5	6	7	8
K	10.29	÷	13.85	÷
D	10.29	5.95724	13.85	.43012563

S	9	10
K	F	$\sin^{-1}$
D	.43012563	25.47553

	S	1	2	3
C	K	2	×	30.65
	D	2	2.	30.65

S	4	5	6
K	÷	10.29	÷
D	61.3	10.29	5.957240039

S	7	8	9
K	13.85	=	INV
D	13.85	.4301256346	.4301256346

S	10
K	sin
D	25.47553349

It is clear from the above sequence that the included angle in the triangle measures 25.48 degrees.

9.5 LOGARITHMS

The modern revolution brought about by the electronic pocket calculator was preceded some 350 years earlier by an equally fascinating invention, namely *logarithms*. It was the invention of logarithms which gave rise to the slide rule. Logarithms permit the rapid solution of a host of complex problems and are indispensable to the study of higher mathematics.

The logarithm of a number is defined as the exponent to which a base must be raised to equal that number. Simply stated, if

$$y = a^x,$$

the logarithm of y to the base a is x. This is conventionally expressed as

$$\log_a y = x.$$

The most commonly used base is 10, and for this reason logarithms expressed in this base are referred to as *common logarithms*.

There is another frequently used logarithm known as the *natural logarithm*. Instead of using 10 as its base, it uses the constant e and is usually denoted as *ln* (pronounced "lan").

Regardless of the base of the logarithm, the following identities apply:

(a) $\log_b x = \dfrac{\log_a x}{\log_a b} = \log_a b \times \log_a x$

(b) $\log(ab) = \log a + \log b$

(c) $\log \dfrac{a}{b} = \log a - \log b$

(d) $\log(a^b) = b \times \log a$

(e) $\log 1 = 0$

(f) $\log_a a = 1$

If

$$y = \log_a x,$$

where both y and a are known values, we can solve the above equation for x, which gives the *antilogarithm* of y to the base a. It follows therefore that

$$x = a^y.$$

For the common logarithm, the antilog is given by

$$x = 10^y$$

and for the natural logarithm by

$$x = e^y .$$

What is the common log of 1000?

Solution:

The problem asks the question, to what power must 10 be raised to equal 1000.

$$1000 = 10^x$$
$$10^3 = 10^x$$
$$x = 3$$

Check:

B or C S   1   2
        K   1000   log
        D   1000   3.

Determine the value of $\log\left(\dfrac{233}{49.7}\right)$, to four decimal places.

Solution:

B S   1   2   3   4   5
   K   233   ENT↑   49.7   ÷   log
   D   233   233.   49.7   4.6881287   .6709995

C S   1   2   3
   K   233   ÷   49.7
   D   233   233.   49.7

S	4	5	6
K	=	2nd	log
D	4.688128773	4.688128773	.6709995323

Thus, we find the answer to be .6710, to four decimal places.

Evaluate $y = \dfrac{(1.23)^2 \cos 57.3}{\log \pi}$, to the nearest one hundredth.

Solution:

B	S	1	2	3	4
	K	1.23	ENT↑	F	x^2
	D	1.23	1.23	1.23	1.5129

	S	5	6	7	8
	K	57.3	cos	×	π
	D	57.3	.5402403	.81732954	3.1415926

	S	9	10
	K	log	÷
	D	.4971499	1.6440303

C	S	1	2	3
	K	1.23	x^2	×
	D	1.23	1.5129	1.5129

	S	4	5	6
	K	57.3	cos	÷
	D	57.3	.5402403205	.8173295809

	S	7	8	9
	K	π	2nd	log
	D	3.141592654	3.141592654	.4971498727

S   10
K   =
D   1.644030554

We find from the above that the value of y, to the nearest hundredth, is 1.64.

9.6 ARITHMETIC PROGRESSIONS

One of the ways of understanding systematic progressive change, such as may be found in production output, population increase and decrease, etc., is to consider it as an arithmetic or geometric progression.

A *progression*—also referred to as a *sequence*—is merely a set of ordered numbers formed according to some specific rule. For example, if we are given the set of numbers

$$1, 5, 9, 13, \ldots,$$

by examining them we can deduce that each subsequent number of the set is equal to four more than the previous number. Thus, we can predict that the next number in the above sequence would be 17, the following one 21, etc.

In mathematics, such a set of numbers is called an *arithmetic progression*, and each number of the progression is called a *term*. The difference between each term is known as the *common difference*. In the above progression, the common difference is 4. In the progression

$$15, 10, 5, 0, -5, \ldots,$$

the common difference is -5. Thus, it can be seen that to calculate the common difference in an arithmetic progression, we merely take the difference between two successive terms.

Finding the nth Term of an Arithmetic Progression

To find the last term l of a progression of n terms, with a common difference d and a first term a, the following formula is generally used:

$$l = a + (n - 1)d$$

Given the arithmetic progression 4, 10, 16, 22, . . . , calculate the 10th term.

Solution:
Substituting $a = 4$, $n = 10$, and $d = 6$ in the formula,

$$l = a + (n - 1)d$$
$$= 4 + (10 - 1)6$$
$$= 4 + (9)6$$
$$= 4 + 54$$
$$= 58$$

Finding the Sum of an Arithmetic Progression

The formula usually used to calculate the sum of the terms S of an arithmetic progression is

$$S = \frac{n}{2} (a + l),$$

where a, n, and l are defined as above.

Find the sum of twenty terms of an arithmetic progression whose first term is 1 and whose 20th term is 58.

Solution:

$$S = \frac{n}{2} (a + l)$$

$$= \frac{20}{2} (1 + 58)$$

A S	1	2	3	4	5	6	7	8
K	1	+	58	×	20	÷	2	=
D	1.	1.	58.	59.	20.	1180.	2.	590

Find the sum of the first 15 terms of the following arithmetic progression: 20, 29, 38, 47, 56, . . .

Solution:

In order to apply the formula, we must know the last term of the above progression. Thus, we can rewrite the formula as

$$S = \frac{n}{2}(a + a + (n-1)d)$$

$$= \frac{n}{2}(2a + (n-1)d).$$

In this case, $n = 15$, $a = 20$, and d, the common difference, is $29 - 20 = 9$. Therefore,

$$S = \frac{15}{2}(2(20) + (15-1)(9)).$$

A

S	1	2	3	4	Write down	5	6
K	2	X	20	=	the value of	15	-
D	2.	2.	20.	40.	$2a = 40$.	15.	15.

S	7	8	9	10	11	12
K	1	X	9	+	40	X
D	1.	14.	9.	126.	40.	166.

S	13	14	15	16
K	15	÷	2	=
D	15.	2490.	2.	1245.

B

S	1	2	3	4	5	6	7	8
K	2	ENT↑	20	X	15	ENT↑	1	-
D	2	2.	20	40.	15	15.	1	14.

S	9	10	11	12	13	14	15
K	9	X	+	15	X	2	÷
D	9	126.	166.	15	2490.	2	1245.

C	S	1	2	3	4	5	6	7	8
	K	15	-	1	=	×	9	+	2
	D	15	15.	1	14.	14.	9	126.	2

	S	9	10	11	12	13	14	15	16
	K	×	20	=	×	15	÷	2	=
	D	2.	20	166.	166.	15	2490.	2	1245.

9.7 GEOMETRIC PROGRESSIONS

If the terms of a progression differ by a constant multiplication factor, such as in the sequence

$$1, 2, 4, 8, 16, \ldots,$$

the sequence is then called a *geometric progression*. The constant multiplier is usually referred to as the *common ratio*. This ratio may be found by dividing any term by its preceding term. Thus, in the above progression, the common ratio is

$$\frac{2}{1} = 2.$$

Finding the Last Term of a Geometric Progression

Let us assume that the first term of a geometric progression is a and the common ratio is r. The sequence would therefore be

$$a, ar, ar \times r, ar \times r \times r, \ldots$$
$$\text{or} \quad a, ar, ar^2, ar^3, \ldots$$

In order to find the last term of a geometric progression, we use the following formula, in which l represents the last or nth term:

$$l = ar^{(n-1)}$$

Find the 10th term of the progression $2, 6, 18, \ldots$

Solution:
$l = ar^{n-1}$, where $a = 2$, $r = \frac{6}{2} = 3$, and $n = 10$
$l = (2)(3)^9$.

A   S   1   2   3   4   5

      K   3   X   =   =   X

      D   3.   3.   9.   27.   27.

      S   6   7   8   9   10

      K   =   =   X   2   =

      D   729.   19683.   19683.   2.   39366.

B   S   1   2   3   4   5   6

      K   3   ENT↑   9 y^x 2   X

      D   3   3.   9   19683.02   2   39366.04

C   S   1   2   3   4   5   6

      K   3 y^x 9   X   2   =

      D   3   3.   9   19683.   2   39366.

The answer to the above problem is 39366, which may be obtained directly when using the basic calculator. Using the constant multiplication technique discussed at the beginning of this book, we calculate 3^9 as $(3^3)^3$ and multiply the result by 2.

Using the intermediate calculator, the 3 is raised to the power 9 by pressing the y^x key. This has the effect of computing the result by means of logarithms, and as a consequence, a small computational discrepancy is incurred. Even though this same procedure is adopted when solving the problem with the advanced calculator, we nevertheless arrive at the right answer. The difference is due to the greater accuracy of the SR-51.

Finding the Sum of a Geometric Progression

The sum S of a geometric progression containing n terms is generally computed using either of the following two formulas:

$$S = \frac{a - ar^n}{1 - r} \quad \text{or} \quad S = \frac{a - rl}{1 - r}$$

Find the sum of the first ten terms of the following geometric progression: 128, 64, 32, 16, . . .

Solution:

In the above progression, we calculate the common ratio r as $\frac{1}{2}$. The value of a is 128 and the value of n is 10. We can therefore compute the sum using the formula:

$$S = \frac{a - ar^n}{1 - r}$$

$$= \frac{128 - 128(\frac{1}{2})^{10}}{1 - \frac{1}{2}}$$

A	S	1	2	3	4
	K	.5	X	=	X
	D	0.5	0.5	0.25	0.25

	S	5	6	7	8
	K	=	=	=	=
	D	0.065	0.015625	0.0039062	0.0009765

	S	9	10	11	12
	K	X	128	=	–
	D	0.0009765	128.	0.124992	0.124992

	S	13	14	15	16
	K	=	128	=	÷
	D	0	128.	127.87501	127.87501

	S	17	18		
	K	.5	=		
	D	0.5	255.75002		

B	S	1	2	3	4	5
	K	.5	ENT↑	10	y^x	128
	D	.5	.5	10	.0009766	128

	S	6	7	8	9	10
	K	×	128	$x \leftrightarrow y$	−	.5
	D	.125004	128	.125004	127.875	.5

	S	11
	K	÷
	D	255.75

C	S	1	2	3	4
	K	.5	y^x	10	×
	D	0.5	0.5	10	.0009765625

	S	5	6	7	8
	K	128	=	STO	1
	D	128	0.125	0.125	0.125

	S	9	10	11	12
	K	128	−	RCL	1
	D	128	128.	128.	0.125

	S	13	14	15	16
	K	=	÷	.5	=
	D	127.875	127.875	.5	255.75

Using the basic calculator, we find that although the result is given as 255.75002, the .00002 is a computational inaccuracy and should be ignored. A point worth mentioning in the basic calculator sequence is that $(\frac{1}{2})^{10}$ is computed as $((\frac{1}{2})^2)^5$, using the constant multiplication feature. The constant is further exploited in the calculation of the difference of the two terms in the numerator.

9.8 INVESTMENT PROBLEMS

Not only are investment problems important in themselves, but they prove to be fascinating to a great number of students. Furthermore, they have direct applicability to problems of everyday life.

To compute the amount of money that will result from an investment of P dollars, at the annual investment rate of $r\%$, for a period of n years, we can use the compound interest formula:

$$\text{amount} = P(1 + r)^n$$

Calculate the amount of money that will result from investing a sum of \$3500 in an account for 8 years, if interest is compounded annually at the rate of 6%.

Solution:

$$\text{amount} = P(1 + r)^n,$$
where $P = 3500$, $r = 6\% = .06$,
and $n = 8$
$$\text{amount} = 3500\,(1 + .06)^8$$
$$= 3500\,(1.06)^8$$

A	S	1	2	3	4
	K	1.06	×	=	×
	D	1.06	1.06	1.1236	1.1236

	S	5	6	7	8
	K	=	×	=	×
	D	1.2624769	1.2624769	1.5938479	1.5938479

	S	9	10
	K	3500	=
	D	3500	5578.4676

B	S	1	2	3	4	5	6
	K	1.06	ENT↑	8	y^x	3500	×
	D	1.06	1.06	8	1.593847	3500	5578.4645

C	S	1	2	3	4	5	6
	K	1.06	y^x	8	X	3500	=
	D	1.06	1.06	8	1.593848075	3500	5578.468261

The compounded amount therefore equals \$5578.47. On the basic calculator, 1.06^8 was calculated as $(((1.06)^2)^2)^2$, advantage being taken of the constant feature.

Find the principal that must be invested at 6.25% interest compounded quarterly in order for the yield in 5 years to be \$1000.

Solution:

$$A = P(1 + r)^n,$$

where $A = 1000$, $r = 6.25\% = \dfrac{.0625}{4}$ per interest period

$$= 0.015625$$

$n = 5$ years $\times$ 4 quarters per year $= 20$

$$1000 = P(1.0625)^{20}$$

$$P = \frac{1000}{(1.015625)^{20}}$$

A	S	1	2	3	4
	K	1.015625	X	=	X
	D	1.015625	1.015625	1.0314941	1.0314941

	S	5	6	7	8
	K	=	X	=	=
	D	1.06398	1.06398	1.1320534	1.2044821

	S	9	10	11	12
	K	=	=	÷	=
	D	1.2815448	1.363538	1.363538	1.

	S	13	14
	K	1000	=
	D	1000.	733.38623

B
S	1	2	3	4
K	1.015625	ENT↑	20	y^x
D	1.015625	1.015625	20	1.0363538

S	5	6	7
K	1000	$x \leftrightarrow y$	÷
D	1000	1.363538	733.38623

C
S	1	2	3
K	1.015625	y^x	20
D	1.015625	1.015625	20

S	4	5	6
K	÷	1000	$x \lessgtr y$
D	1.363539279	1000	1.363539279

S	7
K	=
D	733.38855468

In accordance with the three sequences above, \$733.39 must be invested at $6\frac{1}{4}\%$, compounded quarterly, in order to yield \$1000 in five years. Using the basic calculator, $(1.015625)^{20}$ is calculated as $(((1.015625)^2)^2)^5$. Once this is calculated, the denominator can be made into a constant division factor in order to complete the required division. Using the intermediate calculator, the $x \leftrightarrow y$ key was used to "flip" the two operands before proceeding with the division; the same was done using the advanced calculator.

A person is given a choice of investing his graduation gift of \$1500 in one of two different accounts. In Bank X, this principal will be compounded quarterly at $7\frac{1}{4}\%$ per annum over a period of three years. In Bank Y, however, it will be compounded semiannually at $7\frac{7}{8}\%$ per annum over the same three-year period. Which bank offers the most advantageous deal, and by what amount?

Solution:

Bank X

$A_1 = P(1 + r)^n$, where $P = 1500$,

$r = 7\frac{1}{4}\%$ per annum $= \dfrac{.0725}{4}$ per interest period

   $= 0.018125$, and

$n = 3 \times 4 = 12$

$A_1 = 1500 (1.0725)^{12}$

Bank Y

$A_2 = P(1 + r)^n$, where $P = 1500$,

$r = 7\frac{7}{8}\%$ per annum $= \dfrac{.07875}{2}$ per interest period

   $= 0.039375$, and

$n = 3 \times 2 = 6$

$A_2 = 1500 (1.07875)^6$

A	S	1	2	3	4
	K	1.018125	X	=	X
	D	1.018125	1.018125	1.0365785	1.0365785

	S	5	6	7	8
	K	=	X	=	=
	D	1.0744949	1.0744949	1.1545392	1.2405464

	S	9	10	11	Write down
	K	X	1500	=	this amount
	D	1.2405464	1500.	1860.8196	$A_1 = 1860.82$

	S	12	13	14	15
	K	1.039375	X	=	X
	D	1.039375	1.039375	1.0803003	1.0803003

S	16	17	18	19
K	=	=	×	1500
D	1.1670487	1.260763	1.260763	1500.

S	20	21	22	23
K	=	–	1860.82	=
D	1891.1445	1891.1445	1860.82	30.3245

B

S	1	2	3	4
K	1.018125	ENT↑	12	y^x
D	1.018125	1.018125	12	1.249546

S	5	6	7	8
K	1500	×	MS	1.039375
D	1500	1860.819	1860.819	1.039375

S	9	10	11	12
K	ENT↑	6	y^x	1500
D	1.039375	6	1.260763	1500

S	13	14	15
K	×	MR	–
D	1891.1445	1860.819	30.3255

C

S	1	2	3
K	1.018125	y^x	12
D	1.018125	1.018125	12

S	4	5	6
K	×	1500	=
D	1.240546991	1500	1860.820487

S	7	8	9
K	STO	1	1.039375
D	1860.820487	1860.820487	1.039375

S	10	11	12
K	y^x	6	X
D	1.039375	6	1.260763419

S	13	14	15
K	1500	=	–
D	1500	1891.145129	1891.145129

S	16	17	18
K	RCL	1	=
D	1891.145129	1860.820487	30.32464172

From the sequences above, we find that $1500 invested in Bank X will amount to $1860.82 after three years, while the same amount invested in Bank Y yields $1891.14 for the same time period. This is a difference of about $30.32 between the two banks. It is quite clear in which bank the money should be invested.

9.9 EXERCISES

1. Verify that the trigonometric identity

$$\sin 2x = 2 \sin x \cos x$$

holds for the angles (a) $30°$, (b) $\pi/4$, (c) $10.57°$.

2. In triangle ABC, $\sin A = .7071$, $\sin B = .7660$, and $a = 3.972$. Calculate b.

3. In triangle ABC, $b = 6.98$, $c = 4.6$ and $\cos A = .4876$. Calculate a.

4. Find the value of angle B in triangle ABC if $a = 3.46$, $b = 2.18$, and $c = 1.97$.

5. Calculate the area of a triangle whose two sides measure 13.4 and 12.8 and whose included angle measures $33°$.

6. Calculate the area of triangle ABC shown below, given $\sin C = 0.9848$ and $\cos A = 0.64279$.

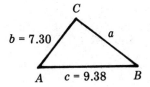

(*Hint:* Either use the Law of Cosines to calculate a and then use the area formula or else calculate sin A by applying the identity $\sin^2 A + \cos^2 A = 1$ and then use the area formula.)

7. Evaluate:

(a) $\dfrac{\log 4.879 - \log 27.86}{\log (32.189)}$

(b) $\log (3.689^5) + \log 2.87$

(c) $\dfrac{\log (58.57 \times 36.29)}{\log 82.9 - 3.86}$

(d) antilog 3.27

8. Calculate the 15th term of the following arithmetic progression: 1, 5, 9, 13, . . .

9. Calculate the sum of the first 50 terms of the following progression: 3, 5, 7, 9, 11, 13, . . .

10. Calculate the sum of the consecutive numbers 1 through 100.

11. Calculate the 11th term of the geometric progression 1, 2, 4, 8, . . .

12. Find the sum of the first 10 terms of the following progression: 4, 12, 36, 108, . . .

10
Chemistry

You may wonder how a calculator can help you with chemistry. After all, mixing compound A with compound B doesn't seem to require very much mathematical computation. Actually, you will discover that the farther you proceed with the study of chemistry, the more you will need mathematical manipulation and computation. This chapter will provide a description and review of those aspects of chemistry for which a calculator is most useful.

It would be a good idea at this point to review the concept of scientific notation and refamiliarize yourself with metric measures, both of which were covered in previous chapters, since physical properties are often expressed in scientific notation, and chemists use the metric system almost exclusively.

10.1 TEMPERATURE CONVERSION

Temperature is a measure of the heat that a substance produces and is expressed in one of the following three scales:

> Fahrenheit (F)
> Celsius (or Centigrade) (C)
> Kelvin (K)

To convert from Fahrenheit to Celsius, or from Celsius to Fahrenheit, the following formula may be used:

$$\frac{C}{5} = \frac{F - 32}{9}$$

If we wish to convert from Fahrenheit to Celsius, we substitute the Fahrenheit temperature for F in the above formula and calculate C as shown.

$$C = \frac{5}{9}(F - 32) \quad \text{or} \quad C = \frac{5F - 160}{9}$$

If, on the other hand, we would like to convert from Celsius to Fahrenheit, we can use the following formula:

$$F = \frac{9}{5}(C + 32) \quad \text{or} \quad F = \frac{9C + 160}{5}$$

To convert from Kelvin to Celsius, or vice versa, we use the formula

$$K = C + 273.$$

1. Convert 85°F to Celsius.

   Solution:

$$C = \frac{5F - 160}{9}$$

$$= \frac{5(85) - 160}{9}$$

A	S	1	2	3	4	5	6	7	8
	K	5	×	85	−	160	÷	9	=
	D	5.	5.	85.	425.	160.	265.	9.	29.444444

C	S	1	2	3
	K	85	2nd	16
	D	85	85	29.44444444

The conversion is done in a straightforward manner when

using the basic calculator, and there is hardly any difference of note using the intermediate calculator. Using the SR-51, however, we may take advantage of the built-in conversion constants, which are listed by number in a table on the back of the calculator. According to the table, to convert from Fahrenheit to Celsius one uses code 16 following the pressing of the key marked 2nd, as indicated in the sequence above. Thus, we find that 85°F equals 29.44°C.

2. Convert 28°C to Fahrenheit.

   Solution:

$$F = \frac{9C + 160}{5}$$

$$= \frac{9(28) + 160}{5}$$

A	S	1	2	3	4	5	6	7	8
	K	9	×	28	+	160	÷	5	=
	D	9.	9.	28.	252.	160.	412	5.	82.4

C	S	1	2	3	4
	K	28	INV	2nd	16
	D	28	28	28	82.4

3. Convert 123°F to Kelvin.

   Solution:
   We use the formulas

$$K = C + 273 \quad \text{and} \quad C = \frac{5F - 160}{9}.$$

Substituting for C and for F gives

$$K = \frac{5(123) - 160}{9} + 273.$$

A	S	1	2	3	4	5
	K	5	X	123	–	160
	D	5.	5.	123.	615.	160.

	S	6	7	8	9	10
	K	÷	9	+	273	=
	D	455	9.	50.555555	273.	323.55555

C	S	1	2	3
	K	123	2nd	16
	D	123	123	50.55555556

	S	4	5	6
	K	+	273	=
	D	50.55555556	273	323.5555556

10.2 BOYLE'S LAW

According to Boyle's Law, the volume of a gas at constant temperature varies inversely with changes in pressure. This means that for a fixed weight of gas, the product of the pressure and the volume at constant temperature will always be a constant. Therefore,

$$PV = K,$$

or more generally, when dealing with either changes in pressure or volume,

$$P_1 V_1 = P_2 V_2.$$

4. 3.48 liters of a gas at constant temperature is under a pressure of 522 millimeters. If the pressure is increased to 730.5 millimeters, what is the new volume of the gas?

Solution:

$$P_1 V_1 = P_2 V_2$$

where $P_1 = 522$, $P_2 = 730.5$, and $V_1 = 3.48$

$$(522)(3.48) = (730.5) V_2$$

$$V_2 = \frac{522 \times 3.48}{730.5}$$

A	S	1	2	3	4	5	6
	K	522	×	3.48	÷	730.5	=
	D	522.	522.	3.48	1816.56	730.5	2.4867351

It is clear from the above that the new volume of the gas is 2.49 liters.

10.3 CHARLES' LAW

According to Charles' Law, the volume of a gas at constant pressure varies directly with its absolute temperature (i.e., $°C + 273°$). This expression can be expressed mathematically as

$$\frac{V}{T} = K.$$

As before, when dealing with problems where the temperature or volume varies, the following more general formula applies:

$$\frac{V_1}{T_1} = \frac{V_2}{T_2}$$

5. 460 milliliters of a gas at constant pressure is subjected to an increase in temperature from $15°C$ to $60°C$. What is the new volume of the gas?

Solution:

$$\frac{V_1}{T_1} = \frac{V_2}{T_2}, \text{ where } V_1 = 460, T_1 = 15 + 273 = 288 \ (°K),$$

$$\text{and } T_2 = 60 + 273 = 333 \ (^\circ K)$$

$$\frac{460}{288} = \frac{V_2}{333}$$

$$V_2 = \frac{460 \times 333}{288}$$

A S	1	2	3	4	5	6
K	460	×	333	÷	288	=
D	460.	460.	333.	153180.	288.	531.875

The new volume of the gas is shown to be 531.875 milliliters.

10.4 THE CALORIE

A *calorie* is defined as the amount of heat required to raise the temperature of 1 gram of water by 1°C. One thousand calories is called a kilocalorie.

6. Calculate the number of calories of heat required to raise the temperature of 35 grams of water from 23°C to 58°C.

   Solution:

$$\text{calories} = 35(58 - 23)$$

A S	1	2	3	4	5	6
K	58	–	23	×	35	=
D	58.	58.	23.	35.	35.	1225.

Thus, 1225 calories are required to raise 35 grams of water from 23°C to 58°C.

10.5 MISCELLANEOUS PROBLEMS

The following problems have been selected as representative of computational chemistry. Each of the problems requires a certain amount of background, and the student is urged to review the material as necessary.

7. The temperature of some water is increased from 18°C to 24°C by adding 300 calories of heat. What is the mass of the water?

Solution:

$$\text{heat gained} = \text{mass} \times \Delta t \times \text{specific heat}$$

$$\text{mass} = \frac{\text{heat gained}}{\Delta t \times \text{specific heat}}$$

$$= \frac{300}{(24 - 18)\,(1)}$$

A	S	1	2	3	4
	K	300	÷	6	=
	D	300.	300.	6.	50.

8. 422 calories of heat is added to 123 grams of acetone at 21°C. If the specific heat of acetone is 0.52, what will be the final temperature of the acetone?

Solution:

$$\Delta t = \frac{\text{heat gained}}{\text{mass} \times \text{specific heat}}$$

$$= \frac{422}{123 \times 0.52}$$

A	S	1	2	3	4	5	6
	K	422	÷	123	÷	0.52	=
	D	422.	422.	123.	3.4308943	0.52	6.5978736

Since the temperature rise is 6.6°C, this figure is added to the initial temperature of 21°C to give the final temperature of 27.6°C.

9. What is the percentage by mass of hydrogen in H_3PO_4? The following atomic weights are given: (a) oxygen = 16, (b) phosphorous = 31, (c) hydrogen = 1.

Molecular weight of $H_3PO_4 = (16 \times 4) + 31 + (3 \times 1)$

$$\% \text{ of hydrogen in } H_3PO_4 = \frac{3}{(16 \times 4) + 31 + 3} \times 100$$

A	S	1	2	3	4	5
	K	16	X	4	+	31
	D	16.	16.	4.	64.	31.
	S	6	7	8	9	10
	K	+	3	÷	3	÷
	D	95.	3.	98.	3.	32.666666
	S	11	12	13	14	15
	K	=	=	X	100	=
	D	1.	0.03061222	0.03061222	100.	3.061222

Hence, the percentage of hydrogen in H_3PO_4 is found to be 3.06%. Notice that the reverse division was calculated and its reciprocal found by the constant feature.

10. Assume that the H_3O^+ ion concentration of a solution is found to be 3×10^{-4} milliliters/liter. Calculate the pH value of the solution.

Solution:

$$pH = \log \left(\frac{1}{(H_3O^+)} \right)$$

$$= \log \left(\frac{1}{3 \times 10^{-4}} \right)$$

In view of the fact that the expression above employs scientific notation, a capability not available on the Novus

Mathematician, we must therefore convert the denominator to standard decimal notation in order to evaluate the expression on the intermediate calculator:

$$3 \times 10^{-4} = 0.0003$$

B	S	1	2	3
	K	.0003	1/x	log
	D	.0003	3333.3333	3.522879

C	S	1	2	3	4	5
	K	3	EE	4	+/-	1/x
	D	3	3 00	3 04	3 -04	3.333333333 03

	S	6	7
	K	2nd	log
	D	3.333333333 03	3.522878745 00

Thus, we find that the pH of the solution is 3.52, to the second decimal place.

11. A solution of acetic acid at 25°C and 0.1 molarity is 1.35% ionized. What is the ionization constant K_i of acetic acid at 25°C?

Solution:

The ionization of acetic acid (CH_3COOH) results in the following equation:

$$CH_3COOH + H_2O = H_3O^+ + CH_3COO^-$$

However, we are told that the acetic acid solution is only 1.35% ionized.

$$0.1M \times .0135 = 1.35 \times 10^{-3}$$

Therefore, 1.35×10^{-3} moles of H_3O^+ and 1.35×10^{-3} moles of CH_3COO^- per liter of solution are produced. The final concentration of CH_3COOH is equal to the original concentration of CH_3COOH minus the ions formed.

$$K_i = \frac{(H_3O^+)\,(CH_3COO^-)}{(CH_3COOH)}$$

$$= \frac{(1.35 \times 10^{-3})\,(1.35 \times 10^{-3})}{.1 - 1.35 \times 10^{-3}}$$

A	S	1	2	3	4
	K	.1	–	.00135	÷
	D	0.1	0.1	0.00135	0.09865

	S	5	6	7	8
	K	.00135	÷	.00135	÷
	D	0.00135	73.074074	0.00135	54128.943

	S	9	10
	K	=	=
	D	1.	0.0000184

Thus, we arrive at the result of 1.84×10^{-5}.

10.6 EXERCISES

1. Convert the following Celsius temperatures to Fahrenheit:
   (a) $62.14°C$ (c) $-40°C$ (e) $100°C$
   (b) $-49.62°C$ (d) $0°C$ (f) $273°C$
2. Convert the following Fahrenheit temperatures to Celsius:
   (a) $62.94°F$ (c) $-112.32°F$ (e) $32°F$
   (b) $114.12°F$ (d) $-40°F$ (f) $212°F$
3. Convert the following Fahrenheit temperatures first to Celsius then to Kelvin:
   (a) $173.2°F$ (c) $0°F$ (e) $-47°F$
   (b) $-23.91°F$ (d) $212°F$ (f) $423°F$
4. 10.123 liters of a gas at constant temperature is under a pressure of 422 millimeters. If the pressure is halved, what will be the new volume of the gas?

5. 20.62 liters of a gas at constant temperature is contained under a pressure of 212 millimeters. If the volume is increased by a factor of 3, what will be the new pressure?

6. 876 milliliters of a gas at constant pressure is subjected to an increase in temperature rising from $11°C$ to $84.5°C$. Calculate the new volume of the gas.

7. Calculate the number of calories of heat required to raise the temperature of 17.35 grams of water from $11.25°C$ to $79.21°C$.

8. If 154 calories of heat raises the temperature of water from $42.5°C$ to $59.5°C$, what is the mass of the water?

9. 53 grams of water had 275 calories of heat added to it. If the final temperature of the water was $30°C$, what was the initial temperature?

10. Calculate the percentage by mass of calcium in $CaCO_3$, where the atomic weight of calcium is 40 and those of carbon and oxygen are 12 and 16, respectively.

11. If the H_3O^+ ion concentration of a solution is found by experiment to be 4×10^{-5} mole/liter, what is the pH value of the solution?

11
Physics

The beginning student in physics is sometimes surprised, if not overwhelmed, by the number of computations which are required before reaching the final solution to a problem. This applies to almost all of the topics in the physics curriculum, as will be seen from the examples given in this chapter. You will also discover that even in elementary physics, the advantages of a scientific calculator, one which goes beyond the capabilities of a simple four-function calculator, are clearly evident. Should you intend continuing your study of physics beyond the beginning course, a sophisticated machine would be a wise investment.

11.1 COMPONENTS OF VECTORS

A *vector* connotes both direction and magnitude. For example, if we were to walk x miles in an easterly direction, and then walk y miles in a northerly direction, we would have walked a total of $x + y$ miles. This distance would be a *scalar* quantity; it has magnitude but not direction. If we were now to ask what our position relative to the starting place is, the answer would have to include both a distance and a direction. These two quantities would produce a *resultant vector*. This vector is represented by the dotted line extending from the starting to the ending point in the following diagram:

165

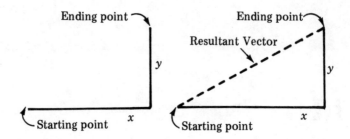

1. An object is displaced 3.45 meters to the east and then 4.56 meters to the north. Compute the resultant vector.

Solution:

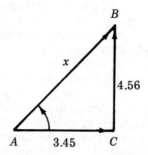

By applying the Pythagorean Theorem, we can compute the length of the resultant vector $\overrightarrow{AB}$ as

$$(3.45)^2 + (4.56)^2 = x^2$$
$$x = \sqrt{(3.45)^2 + (4.56)^2}$$

B	S	1	2	3	4
	K	3.45	F	x^2	4.56
	D	3.45	3.45	11.9025	4.56

	S	5	6	7	8
	K	F	x^2	+	$\sqrt{}$
	D	4.56	20.7936	32.6961	5.7180503

C	S	1	2	3	4
	K	3.45	x^2	+	4.56
	D	3.45	11.9025	11.9025	4.56

	S	5	6	7
	K	x^2	=	$\sqrt{x}$
	D	20.7936	32.6961	5.718050367

The distance x of the resultant vector $\overrightarrow{AB}$ is therefore 5.72 meters. To calculate the direction, which can be expressed as a measure of the number of degrees between the resultant vector $\overrightarrow{AB}$ and the vector $\overrightarrow{AC}$, we can apply our knowledge of trigonometry:

$$\tan A = \frac{\text{opposite}}{\text{adjacent}}$$

$$= \frac{4.56}{3.45}$$

$$A = \tan^{-1}\left(\frac{4.56}{3.45}\right)$$

B	S	9	10	11	12
	K	4.56	ENT↑	3.45	÷
	D	4.56	4.56	3.45	1.3217391

	S	13	14
	K	F	$\tan^{-1}$
	D	1.3217391	52.88962

C	S	8	9	10	11
	K	4.56	÷	3.45	=
	D	4.56	4.56	3.45	1.32173913

	S	12	13
	K	INV	tan
	D	1.32173913	52.88961781

Thus, we have calculated that the resultant vector has a displacement of 52.9°.

2. Calculate the horizontal and vertical components of the velocity of a rocket which is climbing at 4.25 miles per second at an angle of 22.6° to the horizontal.

Solution:

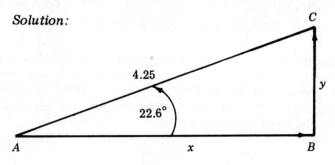

$$\cos A = \frac{x}{4.25}$$

$$\cos 22.6 = \frac{x}{4.25}$$

$$x = 4.25 \times \cos 22.6$$

$$\sin A = \frac{y}{4.25}$$

$$\sin 22.6 = \frac{y}{4.25}$$

$$y = 4.25 \times \sin 22.6$$

B	S	1	2	3	4
	K	22.6	cos	4.25	X
	D	22.6	.9232103	4.25	.39236437

	S	5	6	7	8
	K	22.6	sin	4.25	X
	D	22.6	.3842953	4.25	1.633255

C	S	1	2	3	4	5
	K	4.25	X	22.6	cos	=
	D	4.25	4.25	22.6	.9232102171	3.923643423

	S	6	7	8	9	10
	K	4.25	X	22.6	sin	=
	D	4.25	4.25	22.6	.3842953227	1.633255121

Thus, we find that the horizontal component $\overrightarrow{AB}$ is 3.9 miles per second and the vertical component $\overrightarrow{BC}$ is 1.6 miles per second.

11.2 SOME USEFUL EQUATIONS OF MOTION

Here are some equations which are often used to describe straight line motion that either *starts or stops at rest* and that is *accelerated uniformly*:

$$\text{(a)} \quad a = \frac{v}{t}$$

$$\text{(b)} \quad s = \frac{vt}{2}$$

$$\text{(c)} \quad v^2 = 2as$$

$$\text{(d)} \quad s = \tfrac{1}{2} at^2$$

In these equations,

a = uniform acceleration from rest,
t = time measured from moment of starting,
v = velocity at time t,
s = distance traveled from starting point.

3. A vehicle starts out from rest and accelerates at the constant rate of 8.5 meters/second^2. Calculate the distance traveled by the vehicle at the end of 10.36 seconds.

Solution:

$$s = \tfrac{1}{2} at^2, \text{ where } a = 8.5 \text{ and } t = 10.36$$
$$= \tfrac{1}{2}(8.5)(10.36)^2$$

A	S	1	2	3	4	5
	K	10.36	X	=	X	8.5
	D	10.36	10.36	107.3296	107.3296	8.5

	S	6	7	8
	K	X	.5	=
	D	912.3016	0.5	456.1508

4. An Apollo spacecraft is fired into orbit with an acceleration of 173 miles/hour^2. If the spacecraft travels a distance of 2680 miles, calculate its velocity at this point.

Solution:

$$v^2 = 2as, \text{ where } a = 173 \text{ and } s = 2680$$
$$= 2(173)(2680)$$
$$v = \sqrt{(2)(173)(2680)}$$

C	S	1	2	3	4	5	6	7
	K	2	X	173	X	2680	=	$\sqrt{x}$
	D	2	2.	173	346.	2680	927280.	962.9537891

The spacecraft's velocity is therefore 962.95 miles/hour.

11.3 THE LAW OF UNIVERSAL GRAVITATION

The force of gravitation is directly proportional to the product of the masses of the two objects, and is inversely proportional to the square of the distance between them. This relationship, called the Universal Law of Gravitation, may be expressed by the following equation:

$$F = G \ \frac{m_1 m_2}{d^2},$$

where F = the force of gravity and G = the universal gravitational constant, which has the value 6.67×10^{-11} $\frac{m^3}{kg \ sec^2}$, m_1, m_2 = the mass of the two objects, and d = the distance between the two objects.

5. Calculate the force of attraction between an Apollo and a Mariner spacecraft placed 1500 meters from each other. Assume that the Apollo has a mass of 115000 kilograms and the Mariner a mass of 98575 kilograms. (Since only the advanced calculator has scientific notation, here is the solution as performed on the SR-51.)

Solution:

$$F = G \ \frac{m_1 m_2}{d^2}, \text{ where } G = 6.67 \times 10^{-11},$$

$$m_1 = 115000, m_2 = 98575, \text{ and } d = 1500$$

$$= \frac{(6.67 \times 10^{-11}) \ (115000) \ (98575)}{(1500)^2}$$

C	S	1	2	3
	K	6.67	EE	+/-
	D	6.67	6.67 00	6.67-00

	S	4	5	6
	K	11	$\times$	115000
	D	6.67-11	6.67-11	115000

	S	7	8	9
	K	$\times$	98575	$\div$
	D	7.6705-06	98575	7.561195375-01

	S	10	11	12
	K	1500	x^2	=
	D	1500	2.25 06	3.360531278-07

The force of attraction between the two rockets is therefore 3.36×10^{-7} newtons.

11.4 GRAVITATIONAL PULL

The weight and the mass of an object are interrelated by the equation

$$w = mg,$$

where w = weight of the object, m = mass of the object, and g = gravitational field strength.

The gravitational field strength is equivalent to the acceleration due to gravity, and is constant for any point near the surface of the earth. The pull exerted by gravity acts in a direction towards the center of the earth. Near the surface of the earth the gravitational field strength is 9.8 newtons/kilogram, and this decreases in strength with the square of the distance from the center of the earth.

6. Assuming Neil Armstrong weighed 582 newtons on earth when he made his successful trip to the moon in 1969, calculate his mass and his weight on the moon where g = 1.67 newtons/kilogram.

Solution:

$$m = \frac{w}{g}$$

$$= \frac{582}{9.8}$$

A	S	1	2	3	4
	K	582	÷	9.8	=
	D	582.	582.	9.8	59.387755

Since on the moon the mass is unchanged, we can calculate as follows:

A	S	1	2	3	4
	K	59.39	X	1.67	=
	D	59.39	59.39	1.67	99.1813

Mr. Armstrong's mass would be 59.39 kilograms and he would weigh 99.18 newtons on the moon.

11.5   THE INCLINED PLANE

The force required to pull a frictionless cart at constant speed up an incline that makes an angle of θ with the horizontal is given by the formula:

$$F = mg \sin \theta,$$

where m = mass of the cart and g = gravitational constant. Since $w = mg$, this may be written as

$$F = w \sin \theta.$$

7. What force is required to pull a 40.21-kilogram wheelbarrow up an incline which makes a 27.3° angle with the horizontal? Assume that the wheelbarrow is being pulled at constant speed.

Solution:

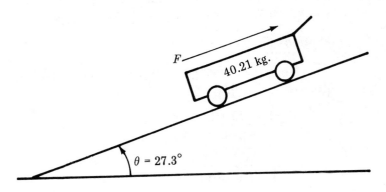

$F = mg \sin \theta$, where $m = 40.21$, $g = 9.8$, and $\theta = 27.3°$
$F = 40.21 \times 9.8 \times \sin 27.3$

B	S	1	2	3	4	5	6
	K	27.3	sin	40.21	$\times$	9.8	$\times$
	D	27.3	.4586496	40.21	18.4423	9.8	180.73454

C	S	1	2	3	4
	K	40.21	$\times$	9.8	$\times$
	D	40.21	40.21	9.8	394.058

	S	5	6	7
	K	27.3	sin	=
	D	27.3	.4586495545	180.7345261

From the above it can be seen that it requires 180.7 newtons to pull the wheelbarrow.

11.6 KINETIC ENERGY

Kinetic energy is the name given to the work done in accelerating an object at rest to any speed. The kinetic energy is usually expressed by the formula,

$$E = \tfrac{1}{2} mv^2$$

8. A parachutist with a mass of 81.64 kilograms has a kinetic energy of 168.26 joules. Calculate the speed with which the parachutist is traveling.

Solution:

$$E = \tfrac{1}{2} mv^2, \text{ where } E = 168.26 \text{ and } m = 81.64$$
$$168.26 = \tfrac{1}{2} (81.64)v^2$$
$$v^2 = \frac{168.26 \times 2}{81.64}$$
$$v = \sqrt{\frac{168.26 \times 2}{81.64}}$$

B	S	1	2	3	4
	K	168.26	ENT↑	2	X
	D	168.26	168.26	2	336.52

	S	5	6	7
	K	81.64	÷	$\sqrt{}$
	D	81.64	4.121999	2.0302706

C	S	1	2	3	4
	K	168.26	X	2	÷
	D	168.26	168.26	2	336.52

	S	5	6	7
	K	81.64	=	$\sqrt{x}$
	D	81.64	4.12199902	2.030270677

11.7 SNELL'S LAW

According to Snell's Law, the ratio of the sines of the angle of incidence and the angle of refraction is constant, and is equal to the ratio of the two velocities. This constant is called the relative index of refraction. Snell's Law is generally represented by the equation

$$\frac{v_i}{v_r} = \frac{\sin \theta_i}{\sin \theta_r},$$

where v_i = velocity of the incident ray, v_r = velocity of the refracted ray, θ_i = angle of incidence, and θ_r = angle of refraction.

9. A beam of light passes from air to liquid X, making an angle of 52.73° with the normal in the air and an angle of 22.5° with the normal in the liquid. Calculate the speed of light in liquid X. Assume that the difference between the speed of light in air and in a vacuum is negligible. The speed of light in a vacuum is 3×10^8 meters/second.

Solution:

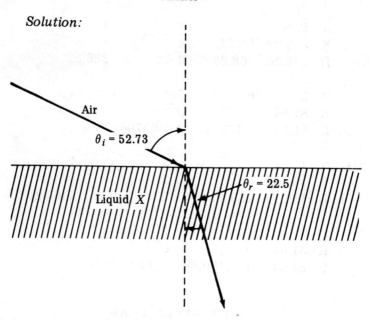

$$\frac{v_i}{v_r} = \frac{\sin \theta_i}{\sin \theta_r}, \text{ where } v_i = 3 \times 10^8,$$

$$\theta_i = 52.73, \ \theta_r = 22.5$$

$$\frac{3 \times 10^8}{v_r} = \frac{\sin 52.73}{\sin 22.5}$$

$$v_r = \frac{3 \times 10^8 \times \sin 22.5}{\sin 52.73}$$

C	S	1	2	3	4
	K	3	EE	8	×
	D	3	3 00	3 08	3. 08
	S	5	6	7	8
	K	22.5	sin	÷	52.73
	D	22.5	3.826834324-01	1.148050297 08	52.73

S	9	10
K	sin	=
D	7.957906666-01	1.442653634 08

We have calculated the speed of light in the liquid on the advanced calculator to be 1.44×10^8 meters/second. (Did you remember to switch the R/D switch to degrees?)

11.8 RAY OPTICS

If an image of an object is produced by means of a lens, the size of the image and its distance from the focal point of the lens may be calculated by the formula

$$\frac{S_o}{S_i} = \frac{D_o}{D_i},$$

where S_o = object size, S_i = image size, D_o = object distance, and D_i = image distance.

The relationship between the focal length f of a lens and the object and image distances is expressed by the formula

$$\frac{1}{f} = \frac{1}{D_o} + \frac{1}{D_i}.$$

10. An illuminated body standing 5.6 centimeters high is placed 25.22 centimeters in front of a lens whose focal length is 6.6 centimeters. Determine the size of the image and its distance from the lens.

Solution:

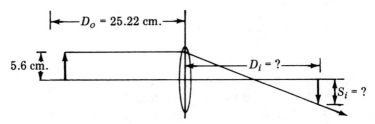

$$\frac{1}{f} = \frac{1}{D_o} + \frac{1}{D_i}, \text{ where } f = 6.6 \text{ and } D_o = 25.22$$

$$\frac{1}{6.6} = \frac{1}{25.22} + \frac{1}{D_i}$$

$$\frac{1}{D_i} = \frac{1}{6.6} - \frac{1}{25.22}$$

B

S	1	2	3
K	6.6	1/x	25.22
D	6.6	.15151515	25.22

S	4	5	6
K	1/x	–	1/x
D	.03965107	.11186408	8.93942

C

S	1	2	3	4
K	6.6	1/x	–	25.22
D	6.6	.1515151515	.1515151515	25.22

S	5	6	7
K	1/x	=	1/x
D	.0396510706	.1118640809	8.939419979

$$\frac{S_o}{S_i} = \frac{D_o}{D_i}, \text{ where } S_o = 5.6, \ D_o = 25.22, \text{ and } D_i = 8.94$$

$$\frac{5.6}{S_i} = \frac{25.22}{8.94}$$

$$S_i = \frac{5.6 \times 8.94}{25.22}$$

A

S	1	2	3	4	5	6
K	5.6	×	8.94	÷	25.22	=
D	5.6	5.6	8.94	50.064	25.22	1.9850911

Thus, we have found that the distance of the image from the lens is 8.94 centimeters and that the size of the image is 1.99 centimeters.

11.9 COULOMB'S LAW

Coulomb's Law may be stated in two parts:

(i) The force of attraction or repulsion between two objects varies directly as the product of the two charges.

(ii) the force of attraction or repulsion between two objects varies inversely to the distance between them (if the objects are spherical, the distance is measured from their centers).

Both these relationships are implied by Coulomb's Law which may be expressed mathematically as

$$F = k\,\frac{q_1\,q_2}{d^2},$$

where F = electric force, $q_1 q_2$ = the two charges, d = distance between the objects, and k = electrostatic constant of free space = 9.0×10^9 newton-meter^2/coulomb^2.

11. Calculate the electric force between two charged points, one of which has a charge of 4.38×10^{-11} coulombs and the other -6.25×10^{-7} coulombs. The distance separating them is .212 meters.

Solution:

$F = k\,\dfrac{q_1 q_2}{d^2}$, where $k = 9.0 \times 10^9$, $q_1 = 4.38 \times 10^{-11}$,

$\quad q_2 = -6.25 \times 10^{-7}$, and $d = .212$

$\quad = \dfrac{(9.0 \times 10^9)\,(4.38 \times 10^{-11})\,(-6.25 \times 10^{-7})}{(.212)^2}$

C	S	1	2	3	4
	K	9	EE	9	×
	D	9	9 00	9 09	9. 09

S	5	6	7	8
K	4.38	EE	+/-	11
D	4.38	4.38 00	4.38-00	4.38-11

S	9	10	11	12
K	$\times$	6.25	+/-	EE
D	3.942-01	6.25	-6.25	-6.25 00

S	13	14	15	16
K	+/-	7	$\div$	.212
D	-6.25-00	-6.25-07	-2.46375-07	0.212

S	17	18
K	x^2	=
D	4.4944-02	-5.481821823-06

Since the solution -5.48×10^{-6} newtons is negative, this implies a force of attraction. (A positive solution would have indicated a force of repulsion.)

12. Two charged spheres A and B have centers separated by a distance of 6.5 meters. If A carries a charge of $+4.0 \times 10^{-8}$ coulombs and B carries a charge of -4.0×10^{-7} coulombs, what is the electric force between them?

Solution:

$$F = k \frac{q_1 q_2}{d^2}, \text{ where } k = 9.0 \times 10^9, \; q_1 = 4 \times 10^{-8},$$

$$q_2 = -4 \times 10^{-7}, \text{ and } d = 6.5$$

$$= \frac{(9.0 \times 10^9)(4 \times 10^{-8})(-4 \times 10^{-7})}{(6.5)^2}$$

C S	1	2	3	4	5
K	9	EE	9	$\times$	4
D	9	9 00	9 09	9. 09	4

S	6	7	8	9	10
K	EE	+/-	8	X	4
D	4 00	4-00	4-08	3.6 02	4

S	11	12	13	14	15
K	+/-	EE	+/-	7	÷
D	-4	-4 00	-4-00	-4-07	-1.44-04

S	16	17	18
K	6.5	x^2	=
D	6.5	4.225 01	-3.408284024-06

The two spheres therefore have an attraction force of -3.4×10^{-6} newtons between them.

11.10 PARALLEL CIRCUITS

If a series of resistors are connected together such that they all have the same potential difference across them as the battery supplying the voltage to the circuit, they are said to be connected in parallel. Under such circumstances, the total resistance of the circuit R_t may be expressed by the formula

$$\frac{1}{R_t} = \frac{1}{R_1} + \frac{1}{R_2} + \ldots + \ldots + \frac{1}{R_n},$$

where $R_1, \ldots, R_n$ = the individual resistances.

13. In the circuit shown below, R_1 = 25 ohms, R_2 = 37 ohms, and R_3 = 400 ohms. Calculate the total resistance of the circuit.

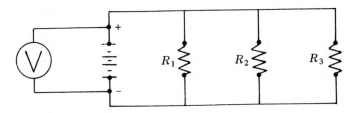

Solution:

$$\frac{1}{R_t} = \frac{1}{R_1} + \frac{1}{R_2} + \frac{1}{R_3}$$

$$\frac{1}{R_t} = \frac{1}{25} + \frac{1}{37} + \frac{1}{400}$$

A	S	1	2	3	4	Write
	K	1	÷	25.	=	down
	D	1.	1.	25.	0.04	this
						result.
	S	5	6	7	8	Write
	K	1	÷	37	=	down
	D	1.	1.	37.	0.027027	this,
						too.
	S	9	10	11	12
	K	1	÷	400	+
	D	1.	1.	400.	0.0025
	S	13	14	15	16
	K	.04	+	.027027	=
	D	0.04	0.0425	0.027027	0.069527
	S	17	18	19	
	K	÷	=	=	
	D	0.069527	1.	14.382901	

The total resistance R_t of the above circuit is therefore 14.38 ohms.

11.11 EXERCISES

1. An object is displaced 20 meters east and 10 meters at 120° from the horizontal. Find the magnitude and direction of the resultant of the two displacement vectors.

2. A force of 50 newtons pulls at an angle of 40° to the x axis. Find its x and y components (i.e., its horizontal and vertical components).

3. The speed of an object increases uniformly from 173 meters per second to 199 meters per second in 5.4 seconds. Calculate the object's acceleration during this interval.

4. A rocket rises vertically with an acceleration of 143 meters per second^2. How much time will be required for the rocket to reach an altitude of 6284 meters?

5. A car weighing 907 kilograms exerts a force on a man weighing 67 kilograms standing 42 meters from the car. Calculate this force of attraction.

6. What force is required to pull an 11 kilogram sled up a hill that has an incline of 37°?

7. If the kinetic energy of a 37 kilogram mass is 103 joules, what is its velocity?

8. A beam of light passing from air to liquid makes an angle of 23.5° with the liquid. Assuming that the speed of light in air is 3×10^8 meters/second, find the angle of refraction.

9. If an object is 0.29 meters from the lens and the focal length of the lens is 0.17 meters, how far from the lens will the image be located?

10. Two conducting spheres are separated by a distance of 2.5 meters between their centers. One sphere has a charge of 1.8×10^{-4} coulombs and the other has a charge of 6.2×10^{-4} coulombs. What is the force that these two spheres exert upon each other?

11. Three resistances are connected in parallel, giving a total equivalent resistance of 6.23 ohms. If the first and third resistors have resistances of 77 and 14 ohms, respectively, calculate the resistance of the second resistor.

Appendix
Answers to
Exercises

Chapter 7

7.2
1. 1739.6812
2. 0.12596732
3. 32.861092
4. (a) 414.5296
   (b) 70.56
   (c) 25198.387
5. (a) 28.2744
   (b) 28.029886
   (c) 4947.7033
6. (a) 520.
   (b) 440.36562
7. 15939.767
8. 24.194818
9. (a) 57.6
   (b) -14.4
   (c) 235.26
10. 12.

7.5
1. 225.2691
2. 16.59
3. (a) 21.507343
   (b) 33.501629
4. 35.406107
5. $w = 22$, $l = 27$

7.7
1. $x_1 = -1$
   $x_2 = -5$
2. $x_1 = -2$
   $x_2 = -5$
3. $x_1 = -3$
   $x_2 = -8$
4. $x_1 = -0.67$
   $x_2 = -1.00$
5. $x_1 = -2$
   $x_2 = -2$
6. $x_1 = 3$
   $x_2 = -3$

7.11
1. $2000 at 6%
   $1900 at 5%
2. 200
3. $4200 at 5%
   $8400 at 4%
4. 21 cookies at 6¢
   4 cookies at 10¢
5. 200 miles

Chapter 8

8.12
1.   25.01081366
2.   6.708203932
3.   334.8713029
4.   135
5.   12.24162979
6.   7.852969815
7.   36
8.   1.787176544
9.   39.099648
10. (a) .8294916669
     (b) .8294916669
     (c) 1.492675159
11. area = 6.881344548
     circumference = 9.299114255

Chapter 9

9.9
1.   see examples in section 9.1-2 for details of the computation
2.   4.302859567
3.   6.82
4.   35.487°
5.   46.70824364
6.   26.22699493 by calculating sin A from the identity, or 25.98356394 by using The Law of Cosines
7.   (a) -.5018548369
     (b) 3.292425173
     (c) -1.713909685
     (d) 1862.087137
8.   57
9.   2600
10. 5050
11. 1024
12. 1023

Chapter 10

1. (a) 143.85°F
   (b) -57.32°F
   (c) -40°F
   (d) 32°F
   (e) 212°F
   (f) 523.4°F
2. (a) 17.19°C
   (b) 45.62°C
   (c) -80.18°C
   (d) -40°C
   (e) 0°C
   (f) 100°C
3. (a) 78.44°C; 351.44°K
   (b) -31.06°C; 241.94°K
   (c) -17.78°C; 255.22°K
   (d) 100°C; 373°K
   (e) -43.89°C; 229.11°K
   (f) 217.22°C; 490.22°K
4. 20.246 liters
5. 70.667 millimeters
6. 1102.71 milliliters
7. 1179.12 calories
8. 9.06 grams
9. 24.81°C
10. 40%
11. 4.4

Chapter 11

1. 17.3 meters and 30°
2. the x component is 38.3 newtons and the y component is 32.15 newtons
3. 4.81 meters per second^2
4. 9.375 seconds
5. 2.3×10^{-9} newtons
6. 64.88 newtons
7. 2.36 meters per second
8. 8.18°
9. .41 meters
10. 1.61×10^2 newtons
11. 13.14 ohms

Index